AS Accounting for AQA
Question Bank

David Cox

Michael Fardcn

osborne
BOOKS

Published by Osborne Books Limited
Unit 1B Everoak Estate
Bromyard Road
Worcester WR2 5HP
Tel 01905 748071
Email books@osbornebooks.co.uk
Website www.osbornebooks.co.uk

Graphic design by Richard Holt

Printed and bound by CPI Group (UK) Ltd, Croydon, CR0 4YY

British Library Cataloguing in Publication Data
A catalogue record for this book is available from the British Library

ISBN 978 1905777 938

MIX
Paper from
responsible sources
FSC® C013604

Contents

Introduction

AS Accounting for AQA Question Bank has been written to provide supplementary examination practice material for students sitting the two AQA AS Accounting examination papers.

The book is divided into two separate sections:

1 **Questions** set out in the style of the AQA examination, with gaps where students can write in the answers.

2 **Answers** to each of the questions.

The book is also arranged in the chapter order of the main text book, **AS Accounting for AQA** (see the Contents on the previous page). There are questions and answers for each of the chapters, with the exception of Chapters 1 to 6, where the questions have been amalgamated into one longer section for ease of use.

David Cox, Michael Fardon

Spring 2012

Acknowledgements

The publisher wishes to thank Jean Cox, Maz Loton and Jon Moore for their help with the production of this book and also Lynn Watkins for her technical editorial work.

Authors

David Cox is a Certified Accountant with more than twenty years' experience teaching accountancy students over a wide range of levels. Formerly with the Management and Professional Studies Department at Worcester College of Technology, he now lectures on a freelance basis and carries out educational consultancy work in accountancy studies. He is author and joint author of a number of textbooks in the areas of accounting, finance and banking.

Michael Fardon has extensive teaching experience of a wide range of banking, business and accountancy courses at Worcester College of Technology. He now specialises in writing business and financial texts and is General Editor at Osborne Books. He is also an educational consultant and has worked extensively in the areas of vocational business curriculum development.

Use of Accounting Terminology

In past years it has been AQA practice in GCE Accounting question papers and mark schemes to operate a dual system where the new IAS (International Accounting Standards) term is given with the UK term in brackets, for example 'inventory (stock)'.

This practice is changing from the January 2013 examinations: AQA will no longer quote dual terminology for commonly used accounting terms, but use only the IAS wording. The relevant IAS terms are set out below, with the old terminology shown in brackets.

- Non-current assets (fixed assets)
- Non-current liabilities (long-term liabilities)
- Inventory (stock)
- Trade receivables (debtors)
- Trade payables (creditors)
- Income statement (trading and profit and loss account)
- Profit for year (net profit)
- Revenue (sales) [where used in income statements]
- Rate of inventory turnover (stock turnover)
- Trade receivables collection period (debtor collection period)
- Trade payables collection period (creditor payment period)

AQA have also stated that in instances where an IAS term has not yet been used in examinations, a new IAS term could be quoted followed by the UK term in brackets, for example 'Statement of Financial Position (Balance Sheet).' The terms that could be used in an examination are shown in the table below.

Current UK term	International term
Accruals	Other payables
Balance sheet	Statement of financial position
Bank and cash	Cash and cash equivalents
Interest payable	Finance costs
Interest receivable	Investment revenues
Investments	Investment property
Land and buildings	Property
Prepayments	Other receivables
Sundry expenses	Other operating expenses
Sundry incomes	Other operating incomes

For the latest information about the use of IAS terminology, please refer to the relevant book pages in the Resources Section of www.osbornebooks.co.uk and www.aqa.org.uk for updating notices.

Practice questions

AS ACCOUNTING

UNIT 1: Introduction to Financial Accounting

QUESTIONS

CHAPTERS 1-6: DOUBLE-ENTRY PROCEDURES; BUSINESS DOCUMENTS

The questions in this section deal with the basics of accounting. They cover topics such as:

- keeping accounting records

- stakeholders in a business

- business documents

- double-entry book-keeping

- subsidiary books

- the trial balance

The reason for grouping them together is that often at this early stage of accounting, examination questions typically cover more than one topic. For later chapters, individual questions have been identified which relate to a particular chapter.

1. Al Porter has started a new business which is financed by £20,000 from his personal savings and a bank loan of £10,000.

    (a)   Explain **two** reasons why Al should keep accounting records.

    Reason 1

    ....

    ....

    ....

    ....

    ....

Reason 2

....

....

....

....

....

(b)   Identify **three** external stakeholders in Al's business. State the interest they will have in the accounting records.

Stakeholder 1

....

....

....

....

Stakeholder 2

....

....

....

....

Stakeholder 3

....

....

....

....

2. Alcaria is a wholesale business. At 1 May 20X4, Sam Brass owed Alcaria £745. During May 20X4, the following transactions took place:

7 May   Alcaria sold goods to Sam Brass for £275.

16 May   Sam Brass returned goods valued at £84 to Alcaria.

24 May   Sam Brass sent a cheque, after deducting a cash discount of £18, to Alcaria to clear the balance owing at 1 May.

(a)   Identify the source document used by Alcaria to record each of the above transactions.

Transaction	Source document
Alcaria sold goods to Sam Brass for £275	
Sam Brass returned goods valued at £84 to Alcaria	
Sam Brass sent a cheque, after deducting a cash discount of £18, to Alcaria to clear the balance owing at 1 May	

(b)   Complete the account of Sam Brass in the books of Alcaria for the month of May 20X4.

Dr   **Sam Brass**   **Cr**

Date	Details	£	Date	Details	£

3. Hayley Ortez runs a clothes shop. Two of her recent business transactions are:

   Item 1: The payment of wages by cheque.

   Item 2: The return of goods to a supplier. The goods had previously been purchased on credit.

   (a) Complete the following table by entering the appropriate details in the spaces provided.

Item	Source document	Account to be debited	Account to be credited
1			
2			

The following transactions took place between Hayley Ortez and Fashion Frocks, a credit supplier, during June 20X1.

1 June	Balance brought forward £1,275
8 June	Goods bought on credit by Hayley Ortez, £950
12 June	Hayley Ortez makes a bank payment to Fashion Frocks for £1,205; cash discount received £70
18 June	Hayley Ortez returns goods to Fashion Frocks, £150
23 June	Goods bought on credit by Hayley Ortez, £650

   (b) Complete the purchases ledger account of Fashion Frocks in the books of Hayley Ortez. Balance the account at 30 June 20X1.

Dr			Fashion Frocks			Cr
Date	Details	£	Date	Details	£

4. Michel Cavares owns a business which sells shoes. The following transactions took place in March 20X9:

(a) Identify the source document for each of the following transactions.

Transaction	Source document
Shoes from a manufacturer purchased on credit	
Michel returned shoes to a manufacturer which had previously been purchased on credit	
Cash and cheques deposited by Michel into the business bank account	
Michel paid a supplier by cheque	
Michel sold 50 pairs of trainers to a sports centre. Payment will be made next month	

(b) Complete the following table by entering the appropriate details in the spaces provided. (Note that Michel's accounting system does not use control accounts.)

Transaction	Account to be debited	Account to be credited
A new shop till purchased from AJ Supplies on credit for £1,000		
£5,000 paid into the business bank account from Michel's savings		
Paid £1,200 to Shoe Traders, a supplier, in settlement of the account balance		
Paid shop rent of £750 by cheque		

5. Assess the usefulness of the trial balance as a means of checking the accuracy of the ledgers.

....

....

....

....

....

....

....

....

....

....

....

....

6. The following is an extract from the cash book of Mark Kirwan for April 20X7.

REQUIRED

(a)   Balance the following bank account at 30 April 20X7, showing the balance brought down on 1 May 20X7, and post cash discounts to the appropriate accounts.

Dr							Cr	
Date **20X7**	**Details**	**Discount** **£**	**Bank** **£**	**Date** **20X7**	**Details**	**Discount** **£**	**Bank** **£**
26 Apr	Balance b/d		246	27 Apr	J Khan		332
27 Apr	A Monro		116	30 Apr	Raven Ltd	16	746
28 Apr	A Syed	10	425				

Bank Account

Dr			Cr	
Date **20X7**	**Details**	**£**	**Date** **20X7**	**Details**	**£**

Discount Allowed

Dr			Cr	
Date **20X7**	**Details**	**£**	**Date** **20X7**	**Details**	**£**

Discount Received

The following are extracts from the day books of Mark Kirwan for April 20X7.

Sales Day Book

Date	Details	Amount
		£
6 Apr	A Monro	316
8 Apr	A Syed	435

Purchases Day Book

Date	Details	Amount
		£
11 Apr	J Khan	454
13 Apr	Raven Ltd	762

REQUIRED

(b)   Post the entries from the sales day book and the purchases day book, and from the bank account, into the accounts below. Balance the accounts at 30 April 20X7, showing the balance brought down on 1 May 20X7 where appropriate.

Dr   **A Monro**   **Cr**

Date 20X7	Details	£	Date 20X7	Details	£

Dr   **A Syed**   **Cr**

Date 20X7	Details	£	Date 20X7	Details	£

Dr					J Khan		Cr
Date 20X7	Details		£	Date 20X7	Details		£
				1 Apr	Balance b/d		332

Dr					Raven Ltd		Cr
Date 20X7	Details		£	Date 20X7	Details		£

CHAPTER 7: THE MAIN CASH BOOK

1. Al Porter has started a new business and has opened a business bank account.
Explain the meaning of each of the following terms in relation to Al's bank account.

(i)   Direct debit

....

....

....

....

....

....

....

....

(ii)   Standing order

....

....

....

....

....

....

....

2. The balances in Sally Henshaw's three column cash book at 3 August 20X7 were as follows:

	£
Cash in hand	286
Bank overdraft	3,472

The following transactions took place

3 Aug	Paid rent by cheque £760
4 Aug	Cash sales £334
5 Aug	Banked £500 cash from the till
5 Aug	Received a cheque of £1,475 from Murphy Ltd in full settlement of a debt of £1,490
8 Aug	Paid rates by direct debit £223
8 Aug	Paid JJ Supplies by cheque £490 after deducting 2% cash discount
10 Aug	Withdrew £400 cash from the bank for business use
10 Aug	Paid wages £480 in cash

REQUIRED

Enter the above transactions in the cash book on the next page and balance the cash book at 10 August 20X7.

Cash Book

Dr									Cr
Date 20X7	Details	Discount £	Cash £	Bank £	Date 20X7	Details	Discount £	Cash £	Bank £

3. Emma Maxwell uses a three-column cash book as part of her double-entry bookkeeping system. The following details relate to March 20X3.

March		£
1	Balance in cash account	200
	Overdrawn bank balance	1,898
2	Bank payment made to Lindum Supplies in settlement of an invoice for £260	254
6	Cheque from Court Ltd paid into bank	1,236
11	Paid rent by cheque	550
13	BACS transfer received from H Sweeney. Discount of £10 had been taken by the customer	896
14	Cash sales	639
27	Paid wages of part-time employee in cash	155
28	Cash sales	786

A bank statement received on 28 March revealed the following additional items.

20	Standing order to Wyvern Council	195
21	Interest charged by bank	45
24	BACS transfer received from Mills and Co Ltd	477

On 31 March, all cash in hand, except a float of £200, was paid into the bank.

REQUIRED

(a) Prepare the cash book, shown on the next page, for the month of March 20X3 from the information provided above.

(b) Balance the cash book at the end of the month and bring down the balances at 1 April 20X3.

(c) Post the discounts to the general ledger accounts shown on the next page.

Dr									
	Emma Maxwell Cash Book								Cr
Date 20X3	Details	Discount £	Cash £	Bank £	Date 20X3	Details	Discount £	Cash £	Bank £

Dr						
	Discount Allowed Account					Cr
Date 20X3	Details	£	Date 20X3	Details	£	

Dr						
	Discount Received Account					Cr
Date 20X3	Details	£	Date 20X3	Details	£	

CHAPTER 8: BANK RECONCILIATION STATEMENTS

1. Jayne Carter has received a bank statement for her business account dated 27 April 20X1. Her cash book showed a debit balance of £743. This did not agree with the closing balance on her bank statement.

    The following entries appear on the bank statement but have not been entered in the cash book.

    (1)   Bank charges of £25

    (2)   A direct debit payment of £220 to Wyvern Council

    (3)   A BACS receipt of £455 from Alportal Ltd

    (4)   A cheque received from L Johnson, returned unpaid by the customer's bank. The cheque for £105 had been debited in Jayne Carter's cash book on 20 April 20X1

    Jayne also discovered that a direct debit for £45 paid to A Alta on 25 April 20X1 appeared on the bank statement correctly, but had been entered in the cash book as £54.

    The following entries appear in the cash book but do not yet appear on the bank statement.

    (1)   A cheque for £126 paid to S Brass on 25 April 20X1

    (2)   Takings of £275 banked on 27 April 20X1

    REQUIRED

    (a)   Make the necessary entries in the cash book of Jayne Carter and bring down the balance at 27 April 20X1. Dates are not required.

Dr		Cash book (bank columns)	Cr
Details	**£**	**Details**	**£**

(b)   Prepare a bank reconciliation statement at 27 April 20X1.

Bank reconciliation statement at 27 April 20X1

....

....

....

....

....

....

....

....

....

(c)   Explain **three** reasons why it is important for Jayne Carter to reconcile her cash book and bank statement balances.

1 ....

....

....

....

2 ....

....

....

....

3 ....

....

....

....

2. The cash book of Susana Villona's business shows a bank overdraft of £2,408 at 30 September 20X4. The balance shown on the bank statement at that date does not agree with the balance shown in the cash book.

The following points are discovered.

(1) A direct debit payment of £485 on 28 September 20X4 to A-Z Finance Ltd has not yet been entered in the cash book.

(2) A cheque payment of £750 on 29 September 20X4 for rent paid has been entered in the cash book but has not yet been presented to the bank.

(3) On 30 September 20X4, the bank debited the account with interest and charges of £124. This amount has not been entered in the cash book.

(4) A cheque received from a customer for £368 on 29 September 20X4 has been paid into the bank and entered in the cash book. The transaction is not shown on the bank statement.

(5) A cheque paid to a supplier on 23 September 20X4 appears on the bank statement as £465 but has been incorrectly entered in the cash bock as £645.

REQUIRED

(a) Make the necessary entries in the cash book of Susana Villona and show the updated balance at 30 September 20X4. Dates are not required.

Dr		Cash book (bank columns)	Cr
Details	**£**	**Details**	**£**

(b)   Prepare a bank reconciliation statement for Susana Villona that clearly shows the balance on the bank statement at 30 September 20X4.

....

....

....

....

....

....

....

....

....

(c)   Explain why Susana Villona's bank may require a copy of her year-end financial statements.

....

....

....

....

....

....

....

....

....

....

....

CHAPTER 9: INTRODUCTION TO FINANCIAL STATEMENTS

1. The following trial balance has been extracted by the book-keeper of Samantha Giardino at 31 December 20X7:

	Dr £	Cr £
Trade receivables	24,365	
Trade payables		19,871
Bank overdraft		2,454
Capital at 1 January 20X7		51,283
Revenue (Sales)		188,622
Purchases	110,233	
Inventories at 1 January 20X7	21,945	
Salaries	37,390	
Heating and lighting	4,276	
Rent and rates	6,849	
Vehicles	20,450	
Office equipment	10,960	
Sundry expenses	1,283	
Vehicle expenses	3,562	
Drawings	20,917	
	262,230	262,230

Inventories at 31 December 20X7 were valued at £18,762.

You are to prepare the income statement of Samantha Giardino for the year ended 31 December 20X7, together with her balance sheet at that date.

Samantha Giardino
Income Statement
for the year ended 31 December 20X7

£   £

....

....

....

....

....

....

....

....

....

....

....

....

....

....

....

....

....

....

Balance Sheet as at 31 December 20X7

	£	£	£

....

....

....

....

....

....

....

....

....

....

....

....

....

....

....

....

....

....

2. Alan Castle has part-completed his income statement for the year ended 30 June 20X3.

From the following information:

(a)   complete the income statement for the year ended 30 June 20X3, commencing with gross profit.

	£
Gross profit	55,430
Salaries and wages	47,390
Discount received	210
Office expenses	2,750
Vehicle expenses	6,840
Bank charges	570
Drawings	8,460
Capital	42,170

Alan Castle
Income Statement
for the year ended 30 June 20X3

	£	£
....		
....		
....		
....		
....		
....		
....		
....		
....		
....		
....		
....		

(b)   prepare Alan Castle's capital account as at 30 June 20X3

Dr   **Capital Account**   Cr

Date 20X3	Details	£	Date 20X3	Details	£

3. From the following figures complete the balance sheet for PQ Trading as at 30 September 20X2. Clearly show the non-current and current assets, non-current and current liabilities, and the proprietor's capital.

	£
Profit for the year	24,550
Inventories at 30 September 20X2	16,345
Trade receivables	24,540
Trade payables	21,364
Property	175,000
Office equipment	16,450
Bank overdraft	5,145
Cash	496
Drawings	21,000
Mortgage on business premises	100,000

PQ Trading
Balance Sheet as at 30 September 20X2

£	£	£

....

....

....

....

....

....

....

....

....

....

....

CHAPTER 10: THE GENERAL JOURNAL AND CORRECTION OF ERRORS

1. The bookkeeper of Alcaria has extracted a trial balance at 31 May 20X3. The totals do not agree and the following errors have been discovered.

    (1)   The credit balance on the purchases returns account has been brought down as £345. It should be £354.

    (2)   The purchases account has been undercast by £100.

    (3)   Discount received of £35 has been entered to the debit of the discount received account.

    Make any necessary entries in the suspense account to correct these errors. Clearly show the opening balance on the suspense account and balance the account.

Dr		Suspense account	Cr
Details	**£**	**Details**	**£**

2. Emma Korecki prepared a trial balance at 30 June 20X7. The trial balance totals are shown below.

Debit £364,859   Credit £364,401

She entered the difference in a suspense account and then discovered the following errors.

(1)   The discount allowed account has been overcast by £100

(2)   A bank payment of £68 for vehicle expenses has been recorded as £86 in the vehicle expenses account

(3)   Discount received of £40 has been correctly entered in the cash book but has not been posted to the general ledger

(4)   A bank payment of £175 for office stationery has been debited to office equipment account.

(5)   A cheque for £500 for rent received has been posted to the debit of rent paid account

(6)   Drawings of £350 have been posted to the credit of wages account

REQUIRED

(a)   Enter the difference in the trial balance totals in the suspense account below. Make any necessary entries in the suspense account to correct the errors.

Dr		Suspense account		Cr
Details	**£**	**Details**		**£**

(b)   Complete the following table to identify the **amount**, if any, by which the profit (net profit) for the year of Emma Korecki would be affected by the **correction** of the errors.

Error	Increase profit £	Reduce profit £	No effect on profit (✓)
(1)			
(2)			
(3)			
(4)			
(5)			
(6)			

CHAPTER 11: CONTROL ACCOUNTS

1. The following information has been extracted from the books of Chris Santo for the month of April 20X1.

	£
Purchases ledger balances at 1 April 20X1	33,154
Purchases day book total	42,805
Cash purchases	3,241
Payments to trade payables	37,396
Receipts from trade receivables	46,083
Returns inwards	1,260
Returns outwards	1,532
Discounts allowed	893
Discounts received	741
Debit balance on sales ledger offset against purchases ledger	585
Cheque paid to a trade payable cancelled on 30 April 20X1	842

REQUIRED

(a) Prepare a purchases ledger control account for the month of April 20X1.

Dr			Purchases Ledger Control Account		Cr
Date	**Details**	**£**	**Date**	**Details**	**£**

(b)   Explain how the purchases ledger control account can be used to verify the balances in the purchases ledger.

....

....

....

....

....

....

....

....

....

(c)   Explain **one** limitation of the purchases ledger control account and give **one** example.

....

....

....

....

....

....

....

....

....

2. The following information has been extracted from the books of Jenny Tavira for the month of June 20X1.

	£
Sales ledger debit balances at 1 June 20X1	45,027
Sales day book total	61,322
Sales returns day book total	1,475
Bank receipts from trade receivables	55,396
Cash sales	12,784
Discounts allowed	1,027
Discounts received	648
Debit balance in a sales ledger account offset against a credit balance in a purchases ledger account	824
Trade receivable's cheque dishonoured	345

REQUIRED

(a) Prepare a sales ledger control account fcr June 20X1.

Dr					Sales Ledger Control Account		Cr
Date	**Details**		**£**	**Date**	**Details**		**£**

(b) Explain how the balance on Jenny Tavira's sales ledger control account verifies the accuracy of her sales ledger.

....

....

....

....

....

....

....

(c) Explain **two** types of error that would **not** be identified by preparing a sales ledger control account.

Error 1 ....

....

....

....

....

....

Error 2 ....

....

....

....

....

....

3. Tony Salter owns a business which manufactures shoes. He operates a manual accounting system. The sales ledger control account for the month ended 31 August 20X2 does not agree with the total of the debit balances extracted from the sales ledger.

The following errors have been discovered.

(1)   The balance brought down in the sales ledger control account should have been £18,780

(2)   Discount allowed of £125 had been completely omitted from the books of account

(3)   A bad debt of £220 had been written off, but had not been entered in the sales ledger control account

(4)   The sales day book had been undercast by £1,000

(5)   A debit balance of £175 in the sales ledger had been entered as a contra item in the purchases ledger control account. No entry had been made in the sales ledger control account

(6)   A cheque from a customer for £395 had been dishonoured. This had not been entered in the sales ledger control account

REQUIRED

(a)   Correct the sales ledger control account and balance the account.

Dr			Sales Ledger Control Account			Cr
Date 20X2	Details	£	Date 20X2	Details		£
31 Aug	Balance b/d	18,870				

(b)   State **three** benefits of preparing a sales ledger control account.

....

....

....

....

....

....

....

....

....

....

CHAPTER 12: ADJUSTMENTS TO FINANCIAL STATEMENTS

1. Explain the meaning of the following terms.

   (a) Accrued expenses

   ....

   ....

   ....

   ....

   ....

   ....

   (b) Prepaid expenses

   ....

   ....

   ....

   ....

   ....

   ....

2. Shelley Smith sells carpets. The following balances have been extracted from the books of account at 31 December 20X3.

	£
Balance at bank	3,130
Capital at 1 January 20X3	22,500
Carriage inwards	1,340
Discounts allowed	460
Discounts received	970
Drawings	10,030
General expenses	16,450
Inventories at 1 January 20X3	27,170
Purchases	85,210
Rent and rates	10,160
Returns inwards	490
Returns outwards	1,520
Revenue (Sales)	124,380
Shop fitting – at cost	8,300
– provision for depreciation at 1 January 20X3	4,500
Telephone expenses	1,260
Trade payables	10,130

Additional information

(1)   Inventories at 31 December 20X3 were valued at £29,210.

(2)   The shop fittings are depreciated using the straight-line method over five years. The estimated residual value of the shop fittings at the end of the fifth year is £800.

(3)   Rent unpaid at 31 December 20X3 amounted to £250.

(4)   Annual rates are £1,320. At 31 December 20X3, three months have been paid in advance.

REQUIRED

Prepare the income statement for Shelley Smith for the year ended 31 December 20X3.

Shelley Smith
Income Statement for the year ended 31 December 20X3

	£	£

3. Richard Farley sells sports equipment. The following balances have been extracted from his books of account at 31 March 20X3.

	£
Bank loan (repayable September 20X8)	7,600
Bank overdraft	2,580
Capital account at 1 April 20X2	29,250
Carriage inwards	850
Discounts allowed	180
Discounts received	790
Drawings	15,040
General expenses	11,470
Heating and lighting	2,720
Inventories at 1 April 20X2	24,830
Purchases	76,250
Rent and rates	18,390
Returns inwards	430
Revenue (Sales)	154,360
Shop fitting – at cost	15,200
– provision for depreciation at 1 April 20X2	5,360
Trade payables	6,220
Trade receivables	3,540
Wages and salaries	37,260

Additional information

(1)   Inventories at 31 March 20X3 were valued at £26,450.

(2)   Annual rent of £10,360 has been paid for the year ending 30 September 20X3.

(3)   The shop fittings are to be depreciated using the straight-line method over five years. The estimated residual value of the shop fittings at the end of the fifth year is £1,800.

(4)   On 31 March 20X3 Richard Farley transferred £2,500 from his personal savings into the business bank account. This transaction has not yet been accounted for.

(5)   A bad debt of £240 was to be written off at 31 March 20X3.

(6)   Wages and salaries of £830 for the week ended 31 March 20X3 have not yet been paid.

REQUIRED

(a)   Prepare the income statement for Richard Farley for the year ended 31 March 20X3.

Richard Farley
Income Statement for the year ended 31 March 20X3

	£	£

(b)   Prepare the balance sheet for Richard Farley at 31 March 20X3.

Richard Farley: Balance Sheet at 31 March 20X3

	£	£

4. Susie Leah has prepared the following balance sheet for her business. It contains errors and the totals do not agree.

Susie Leah
Balance Sheet as at 31 December 20X6

	£000	£000
Non-current assets		
Property at cost	220	
Office equipment	60	
		280
Current assets		
Inventories	18	
Drawings	20	
Bank overdraft	6	
Profit for the year	22	
	66	
Current liabilities		
Trade payables	18	
Trade receivables	15	
Prepaid expenses	3	
Office equipment – provision for depreciation	35	
Accrued expenses	2	
	73	
Net current liabilities		(7)
Net assets		273
Capital		
Balance at 1 January 20X6		103
Mortgage on premises (repayable 20X9)		150
		253

Additional information not yet recorded in the books of account

(1) £3,000 rent owed by Susie

(2) A trade receivable paid £2,000 on 31 December 20X6

(3) A bad debt of £1,000 is to be written off at 31 December 20X6

REQUIRED

Prepare the corrected balance sheet of Susie Leah taking account of the additional information.

Susie Leah: Balance Sheet as at 31 December 20X6

	£000	£000
....		
....		
....		
....		
....		
....		
....		
....		
....		
....		
....		
....		
....		
....		
....		
....		
....		
....		
....		
....		
....		

5. Lydia Duarte owns a business selling building materials. She has prepared the following draft income statement for the year ended 30 September 20X5.

	£
Revenue (Sales)	304,400
Cost of sales	(179,600)
Gross profit for the year	124,800
Expenses	(99,800)
Profit for the year	25,000

After completion of the draft income statement, the following balances remain in the books of account.

	£
Accrued expenses	590
Bank overdraft	2,150
Capital at 1 October 20X4	42,440
Drawings	13,760
Inventories at 30 September 20X5	36,430
Loan (repayable 31 December 20X5)	12,000
Prepaid expenses	730
Trade payables	16,150
Trade receivables	24,310
Vehicles — cost at 1 October 20X4	38,500
— provision for depreciation at 1 October 20X4	15,400

Lydia has been told that the following items have not yet been accounted for.

(1) Wages owing at 30 September 20X5 amounted to £1,480

(2) Rent paid in advance at 30 September 20X5 amounted to £1,100

(3) Depreciation is to be provided on vehicles at 20% per annum using the straight-line method

(4) The value of inventories at 30 September 20X5 has been understated by £2,000

(5) A loan repayment of £1,000 appeared on the bank statement on 30 September 20X5, but has not been recorded in the accounting records

(6) A cheque for £800 received from a trade receivable on 30 September 20X5 has not been recorded in the accounting records

(7) A trade receivable's balance of £250 is to be written off as bad

REQUIRED

(a)   Calculate the adjusted profit of Lydia Duarte for the year ended 30 September 20X5 by completing the table below.

	Effect on profit	
	£	£
Profit for the year		**25,000**
1. Wages owing		
2. Rent paid in advance		
3. Vehicle depreciation		
4. Inventories understated		
5. Loan repayment		
6. Cheque received from trade receivable		
7. Bad debt written off		
Adjusted profit for the year		

(b)   Prepare the balance sheet of Lydia Duarte at 30 September 20X5, taking into account all of the information given above

Lydia Duarte: Balance Sheet as at 30 September 20X5

	£	£

6. Explain the treatment of the following in financial statements.

    (a)   private expenses

        ....

        ....

        ....

        ....

        ....

        ....

        ....

    (b)   goods for owner's use

        ....

        ....

        ....

        ....

        ....

        ....

        ....

AS ACCOUNTING

UNIT 2: Financial and Management Accounting

QUESTIONS

CHAPTER 13: BUSINESS ORGANISATIONS

1. Erica owns a shop selling children's clothes. She is a sole trader. She is considering converting her business to a private limited company with herself as the only shareholder.

   Explain **two** advantages and **two** disadvantages, to Erica, of converting her business to a private limited company.

   Advantages

   ....

   ....

   ....

   ....

   ....

   ....

   ....

   Disadvantages

   ....

   ....

   ....

   ....

   ....

   ....

   ....

2.

> Jane and Scott are proposing to start a new business together which requires capital of £70,000. Jane and Scott can contribute £15,000 each.
>
> There is a good chance of making significant profits, but there is also a chance that the business could fail. A friend has advised that they form a private limited company.

Discuss **two** reasons why Jane and Scott should **not** form a private limited company.

....

....

....

....

....

....

....

....

....

....

....

....

....

....

....

....

....

CHAPTER 14: ACCOUNTING CONCEPTS AND INVENTORY VALUATION

1.   (a)   Explain the following **two** accounting concepts.

(i) Prudence

....

....

....

....

....

....

....

....

(ii) Consistency

....

....

....

....

....

....

....

....

(b)   Explain the importance of applying these **two** accounting concepts when preparing the financial statements of a business.

....

....

....

....

....

....

....

....

....

....

....

....

....

....

....

....

....

....

....

....

2.

> Tanya runs a clothing store which sells 'designer' beachwear. At 31 December 20X4, her financial year-end, there are 100 items of the 'Ripcurl' beachwear range left unsold. These had been bought in the spring at a cost of £15 each and Tanya had expected to sell them for £30 each. As there will be changes in the range for next year, these will have to be reduced to a price of £17.50 each. However, in order to sell them Tanya will have to pay extra advertising costs totalling £300.

(a)   Calculate the value of the remaining 'Ripcurl' beachwear range to be included in the closing inventory value at 31 December 20X4.

....

....

....

....

....

....

....

....

(b)   State **one** accounting concept that is applied to the valuation of inventory.

....

3.   Here4U Ltd owns and operates a number of convenience food shops. The trainee accountant has prepared a draft income statement for the year ended 30 June 20X4. She is unsure of the treatment of the following.

(1)   Tickett & Run Certified Accountants audit the financial statements and give tax advice. Their fee for the year ended 30 June 20X4 is estimated to be £7,500. This has not been included in the draft income statement.

(2)   Part of one shop is rented out to a dry cleaning business. Here4U Ltd is owed rent of £1,500 at 30 June 20X4. This has not been included in the draft financial statements.

(3)   Here4U Ltd purchased new shop tills costing £35,000 during the year. These have been included in non-current assets, but depreciation at a rate of 20% per year on cost using the straight-line method has not yet been allowed for.

(4)   Included in the closing inventories were tinned goods at a cost price of £1,000. They would normally sell for £1,800. However, the tins are damaged and can only be sold for £800.

(5)   The trade receivables figure at 30 June 20X4 is £10,500. Included in this amount is £2,000 owed by Trade Caterers Ltd which has gone into liquidation. The accountant of Here4U Ltd is certain that this amount will not be paid.

Complete the table below. For each item, state a relevant accounting concept and the effect any adjustment would have on the profit for the year.

Item	Effect on profit	Concept
(1) Fee for audit and tax advice		
(2) Rent		
(3) Depreciation		
(4) Inventories		
(5) Bad debt		

CHAPTER 15: FURTHER ASPECTS OF FINANCIAL STATEMENTS

1.

> Lily's trade receivables at 31 October 20X8 were £21,040.
>
> The provision for doubtful debts at 1 November 20X7 was £550.80.
>
> She has been advised that she should adjust the provision for doubtful debts to 3% of trade receivables at 31 October 20X8.

(a) Calculate the provision for doubtful debts at 31 October 20X8.

....

....

....

....

....

(b) Calculate the effect the change in the provision will have on Lily's profit for the year ended 31 October 20X8.

....

....

....

....

....

(c) Calculate the net amount of trade receivables to be shown in Lily's balance sheet at 31 October 20X8.

....

....

....

....

....

2.

Karen is a sole trader. The following information was extracted from her ledger accounts at 1 January 20X3:

			£
vehicles	–	at cost	74,000
	–	provision for depreciation	33,500
machinery	–	at cost	37,000
	–	provision for depreciation	12,250

Karen's depreciation policies are:

*   vehicles are depreciated at a rate of 30% per year using the reducing balance method

*   machinery is depreciated at a rate of 20% per year on cost using the straight-line method

There were no purchases or sales of vehicles and machinery during the year ended 31 December 20X3.

(a)   Calculate the amount of depreciation on

(i) vehicles

(ii) machinery

to be included in the income statement for the year ended 31 December 20X3.

....

....

....

....

....

....

....

....

....

....

(b) Show the balance sheet (extract) for

(i) vehicles

(ii) machinery

to be included in the balance sheet at 31 December 20X3.

....

....

....

....

....

....

....

....

....

....

....

....

....

....

....

3. Amy is a sole trader. The following information was extracted from her ledger accounts at 1 July 20X6:

	£
vehicles at cost	46,000
provision for depreciation	22,000

During the financial year ended 30 June 20X7, Amy sold a vehicle for £6,500. This vehicle had originally cost £12,000 and had been depreciated by £5,250. Amy also purchased a new vehicle costing £16,250.

Amy depreciates vehicles at the rate of 25% per annum using the reducing balance method. Depreciation is calculated on vehicles held at the end of the financial year.

(a) Calculate the profit or loss on the sale of the vehicle which has been sold.

....

....

....

....

....

(b) Calculate the depreciation on vehicles to be included in the income statement for the year ended 30 June 20X7.

....

....

....

....

....

4.

Alex Munro owns a retail business. He provides the following information for the year ended 30 April 20X3:

	£
Wages	33,470
Drawings	16,950
Bad debts	255
Administration expenses	24,075
Discount allowed	315
Bad debts recovered	195
Rent received	2,360
Gross profit for the year	86,245

Additional information	**As at 1 May 20X2**	**As at 30 April 20X3**
	£	£
Provision for depreciation of non-current assets	45,000	27,500
Provision for doubtful debts	460	310
Rent receivable paid in advance	–	540

During the year ended 30 April 20X3, a vehicle which had originally cost £12,000 was sold for £3,750. The depreciation on the vehicle was £7,500.

Prepare the income statement of Alex Munro for the year ended 30 April 20X3.

....

....

....

....

....

....

....

....

....

....

5.

Tamsin Smith owns a retail business. She has calculated the gross profit for the year ended 30 June 20X4 as £14,760.

She has a computerised system of inventory control, which automatically updates the inventory records whenever a sale is made. The closing inventory value from the computer system of £10,330 was used in the calculation of gross profit.

On 30 June 20X4, a physical inventory take was carried out and the inventory was valued at £9,760.

The following balances have been extracted from the books of account at 30 June 20X4.

		£
Vehicles	– at cost	32,000
	– provision for depreciation	14,000
Shop fittings –	at cost	17,000
	– provision for depreciation	6,800
Trade receivables		8,310
Provision for doubtful debts		245
Operating expenses		6,240
Rent received		5,600

Adjustments have yet to be made for the following:

(1)   Rent receivable paid in advance at 30 June 20X4 is £650.

(2)   Operating expenses owing at 30 June 20X4 amounted to £495.

(3)   During the year, bad debts recovered amounted to £220.

(4)   At 30 June 20X4, bad debts to be written off amounted to £590.

(5)   Vehicles are depreciated at a rate of 25% per year using the reducing balance method.

(6)   Shop fittings are depreciated at a rate of 20% per year on cost using the straight-line method.

(7)   Tamsin's policy is to maintain the provision for doubtful debts at 2.5% of trade receivables.

REQUIRED

Prepare Tamsin's income statement for the year ended 30 June 20X4.

....

....

....

....

....

....

....

....

....

....

....

....

....

....

....

....

....

....

CHAPTER 16: PREPARING SOLE TRADER FINANCIAL STATEMENTS

1. Anton Buszczak owns a retail business. He provides the following balances from his books for the year ended 30 June 20X6:

	£
Purchases	59,450
Revenue (Sales)	145,630
Inventory at 1 July 20X5	4,525
Vehicle running expenses	3,965
Rent and rates	12,080
Office expenses	6,335
Discounts allowed	580
Wages and salaries	43,190
Machinery – cost	25,000
– provision for depreciation	11,000
Vehicles – cost	33,000
– provision for depreciation	12,200
Trade receivables	4,155
Trade payables	10,845
Capital	28,550
Drawings	12,580
Cash and cash equivalents (Bank)	3,365

Adjustments have yet to be made for the following:

(1)   closing inventory of £5,385

(2)   office expenses owing £345

(3)   vehicle running expenses prepaid £175

(4)   depreciation of machinery for the year £4,000

(5)   depreciation of vehicles for the year £8,500

REQUIRED

Prepare the income statement of Anton Buszczak for the year ended 30 June 20X6, together with his balance sheet at that date.

2. The following balances have been extracted from the books of Samantha Martinez at 30 September 20X4:

	£	£
Capital		160,500
Revenue (Sales)		245,084
Purchases	156,027	
Office salaries	50,133	
Rates and insurances	6,433	
Administration expenses	17,122	
Bad debts	295	
Provision for doubtful debts 1 October 20X3		645
Bad debts recovered		176
Property at cost	220,000	
Office equipment at cost	45,000	
Provisions for depreciation 1 October 20X3:		
Property		39,600
Office equipment		16,500
Trade receivables and Trade payables	18,400	13,125
Inventory at 1 October 20X3	5,893	
Drawings	22,150	

Additional information at 30 September 20X4 not yet included by Samantha:

(1) Closing inventory £7,541

(2) Office salaries owing £510

(3) Insurance prepaid £232

(4) During the year, Samantha took goods to the value of £750 from the business for her private use

(5) Samantha maintains a provision for doubtful debts of 3% of trade receivables outstanding at the year end

(6) Samantha provides for depreciation of non-current assets as follows:

  property at 2% per year on cost using the straight-line method;

  office equipment 25% per year using the reducing balance method.

REQUIRED

(a) Prepare Samantha's income statement for the year ended 30 September 20X4.

(b) Prepare an extract from Samantha's balance sheet as at 30 September 20X4 showing the capital section only.

3.

Charlotte Lee is preparing the financial statements for her business for the year ended 31 December 20X5. The trading section of the income statement shows a gross profit of £67,386.

Charlotte Lee has extracted the following balances from the business books of account in order to complete the income statement:

	£
Rent received	7,864
Bad debts	245
Operating expenses	32,149
Wages	40,231
Fixtures and fittings at cost (1 January 20X5)	18,300
Vehicle at cost (1 January 20X5)	15,000
Provision for depreciation – vehicle (1 January 20X5)	5,400
Trade receivables (31 December 20X5)	24,200
Provision for doubtful debts (1 January 20X5)	810

Additional information

(1)   Included in Charlotte Lee's closing inventory were goods which cost £400. These have been damaged and will have to be destroyed.

(2)   Charlotte has taken goods for her own use from the business. The goods cost £620 and would have been sold for £1,120.

(3)   Charlotte rents part of her property to another business and she has been prepaid January's rent of £620 at 31 December 20X5.

(4)   Included in the total for operating expenses is £295 paid for the year ended 31 December 20X6 and a payment of £6,500 for the purchase of fixtures.

(5)   Wages for the final week of December 20X4 amounting to £456 had not been paid at 31 December 20X5.

(6)   Charlotte sold the vehicle on 30 April 20X5. She received £7,950. She had purchased the vehicle on 1 January 20X3. It is her policy to depreciate the vehicle using the reducing balance method at the rate of 20% per annum. A full year's depreciation is charged in the year of disposal.

(7)   Fixtures and fittings are depreciated using the straight-line method at the rate of 20% per annum on cost.

(8)   It is Charlotte's policy to maintain the provision for doubtful debts at 4% of trade receivables.

REQUIRED

Prepare the income statement for Charlotte Lee's business for the year ended 31 December 20X5.

4.

The following trial balance has been extracted from the books of account of Henry Dunstone, a sole trader, at 31 March 20X7:

	£	£
Bank overdraft		4,107
Capital at 1 April 20X6		103,856
Discounts	862	741
Drawings	10,124	
Fixtures and fittings at cost	30,400	
Fixtures and fittings – provision for depreciation		9,120
Inventory at 1 April 20X6	33,940	
Machinery at cost	55,500	
Machinery – provision for depreciation		19,980
Operating expenses	35,336	
Provision for doubtful debts		1,045
Purchases and Revenue (Sales)	136,240	283,135
Rent and rates	18,022	
Returns	1,068	
Salaries	93,085	
Trade receivables and Trade payables	57,240	49,833
	471,817	471,817

Additional information

(1) Inventory at 31 March 20X7 was valued at £36,875

(2) During the year ended 31 March 20X7, Henry Dunstone had taken £1,475 of goods for his own use

(3) At 31 March 20X7, salaries due and unpaid amounted to £1,465

(4) Rent paid for the period 1 April 20X7 to 30 June 20X7 amounted to £1,950

(5) The provision for doubtful debts is to be 2.5% of trade receivables at 31 March 20X7

(6) Depreciation on machinery is to be provided using the reducing balance method at 20% per annum

(7) Depreciation on fixtures and fittings is to be provided using the straight-line method at 15% per annum on cost

REQUIRED

Prepare the income statement of Henry Dunstone for the year ended 31 March 20X7, together with his balance sheet at that date.

CHAPTER 17: FINANCIAL STATEMENTS OF LIMITED COMPANIES

1.

The equity section of the balance sheet of Ventura Ltd at 31 March 20X6 is shown below:

Equity	£
Ordinary shares of 25p each fully paid	800,000
Share premium	225,000
Revaluation reserve	185,000
Retained earnings	215,000
	1,425,000

On 1 April 20X6, the directors made a bonus issue of ordinary shares on the basis of 2 new shares for every 5 existing shares held. The directors intend to retain their reserves in their most distributable form.

REQUIRED

(a)   Calculate the number of bonus shares issued.

....

....

....

....

....

....

....

....

....

....

(b)   Prepare the equity section of the balance sheet of Ventura Ltd immediately **after** the bonus issue.

Equity   **£**

....

....

....

....

....

....

....

....

....

....

....

....

....

....

2.

> The directors of Pryce Ltd have to repay a loan of £300,000 in July 20X4. They propose to make a rights issue on 1 May 20X4 on the basis of 1 new share for every 4 shares in issue at a premium of 20p per share.
>
> The share capital of Pryce Ltd at 30 April 20X4 was:
>
> | | £ |
> |---|---|
> | Ordinary shares of 50p each fully paid | 500,000 |

REQUIRED

(a)   Calculate the cash to be received from the rights issue assuming that it is fully subscribed.

....

....

....

....

....

> The directors of Pryce Ltd propose to pay a dividend in September 20X4 of 6p per share based on the shares in issue in September 20X4.

REQUIRED

(b)   Calculate the amount of the dividend to be paid.

....

....

....

....

3. The equity section of the balance sheet of Axiom plc at 30 June 20X4 is shown below:

Equity	£
Share capital (ordinary shares)	600,000
Share premium	90,000
Retained earnings	330,000
	1,020,000

The ordinary shares have a nominal value of 25p each.

On 1 January 20X5, a rights issue of shares was completed. The shares were issued on the basis of 1 new share for every 4 existing shares at the issue price of 40p per share. The issue was fully subscribed.

During the year ended 30 June 20X5, dividends paid totalled £220,000.

The profit for the year ended 30 June 20X5 was £365,000.

Prepare the statement of changes in equity of Axiom plc for the year ended 30 June 20X5. Use the table provided.

Axiom plc

Statement of changes in equity for the year ended 30 June 20X5

	Issued Share Capital £	Share Premium £	Retained Earnings £	Total £
At 1 July 20X4	600,000	90,000	330,000	1,020,000
Issue of shares				
Profit for the year				
Equity dividends paid in the year				
At 30 June 20X5				

4.

The equity section of the balance sheet of Bohan Ltd at 1 January 20X2 is shown below:

Equity	£
Ordinary shares of 50p each fully paid	220,000
Retained earnings	118,000
	338,000

On 1 November 20X2, a rights issue of shares was completed. The shares were issued on the basis of 1 new share for every 2 shares held at a price of 80p per share. The issue was fully subscribed.

During the year ended 31 December 20X2, dividends paid totalled £45,000.

The profit for the year ended 31 December 20X2 was £79,000.

Prepare the statement of changes in equity of Bohan Ltd for the year ended 31 December 20X2. Use the table provided.

Bohan Ltd

Statement of changes in equity for the year ended 31 December 20X2

	Issued Share Capital £	Share Premium £	Retained Earnings £	Total £
At 1 January 20X2	220,000	–	118,000	338,000
Issue of shares				
Profit for the year				
Equity dividends paid in the year				
At 31 December 20X2				

5. The directors of Croft Ltd needed to raise funds to finance the expansion of the business. They decided to make a rights issue of ordinary shares on the basis of 1 new share for every 5 shares held, at a price of £1.60 each. The issue was fully subscribed.

The equity section of the balance sheet, **before** the issue, is shown below.

	£
Ordinary shares of £1 each fully paid	600,000
Share premium	75,000
Retained earnings	128,454
	803,454

REQUIRED

(a) Prepare the equity section of the balance sheet of Croft Ltd immediately **after** the rights issue.

Equity £

....

....

....

....

....

....

....

....

....

(b) Define the term 'capital reserves'. Give **one** example of a capital reserve.

Definition ....

....

....

....

Example ....

....

....

....

(c) Define the term 'revenue reserves'. Give **one** example of a revenue reserve.

Definition ....

....

....

....

Example ....

....

....

....

CHAPTER 18: RATIO ANALYSIS

1. Samantha owns a clothes shop. She is concerned that her closing inventory is much higher than her opening inventory and that the business is becoming inefficient. Last year, her rate of inventory turnover was 8 times.

   She provides the following extract from her income statement for the current year:

	£	£
Revenue	117,950	
Opening inventory	10,350	
Purchases	77,550	
Closing inventory	14,150	
Cost of sales		73,750
Gross profit		44,200

REQUIRED

(a) Calculate the rate of inventory turnover for the current year. State the formula used.

Formula

....

....

....

Calculation

....

....

....

....

....

(b)   Comment on the change in the rate of inventory turnover and explain to Samantha whether or not her business is becoming less efficient.

....

....

....

....

....

....

....

2. The directors of Capper Ltd are concerned that, despite making a profit for the year of £150,220, the company has a large bank overdraft. The following information has been taken from the financial statements at the year end:

	£
Closing inventory	105,630
Trade receivables	162,940
Bank overdraft	77,620
Trade payables	134,230

REQUIRED

(a) (i) Calculate the net current asset ratio (current ratio). State the formula used.

Formula

....

....

Calculation

....

....

....

....

(ii) Calculate the liquid capital ratio (acid test, or quick ratio). State the formula used.

Formula

....

....

Calculation

....

....

....

....

(b)   Evaluate the liquidity position of Capper Ltd as shown by the net current asset ratio and the liquid capital ratio. The industry average ratios are: net current asset 1.8:1; liquid capital 0.9:1.

....

....

....

....

....

....

....

....

....

(c)   Explain to the directors of Capper Ltd how it is possible for a business to make a profit but still have an overdraft.

....

....

....

....

....

....

....

....

....

3. The directors of Burlington Ltd are concerned about the profitability of the business. The income statement for the year ended 30 June 20X6 is shown below.

Burlington Ltd
Income statement for the year ended 30 June 20X6

	£	£
Revenue		240,000
Opening inventory	22,000	
Purchases	172,000	
Closing inventory	26,000	
Cost of sales		168,000
Gross profit		72,000
Less expenses		
Wages	34,300	
Advertising	11,750	
Depreciation	13,950	
		60,000
Profit from operations		12,000
Less Finance costs		2,400
Profit for the year		9,600

REQUIRED

(a) Calculate the gross profit margin. State the formula used.

Formula

....

....

Calculation

....

....

(b)   Calculate the profit in relation to revenue ratio (net profit margin). State the formula used.

Formula

....

....

Calculation

....

....

....

....

(c)   Calculate the rate of inventory turnover. State the formula used.

Formula

....

....

Calculation

....

....

....

....

(d) Discuss the actions which the directors of Burlington Ltd could take to improve each of the ratios calculated in (a) to (c). Explain any problems that these actions might cause the business.

....

....

....

....

....

....

....

....

....

....

....

....

....

....

....

....

....

....

....

....

....

....

4.

The directors of Friel Ltd are assessing the liquidity of the company. In particular they are concerned about the credit they give to their customers. At the same time their suppliers are pressing for earlier settlement of amounts due. Both of these are having an adverse effect on the company's bank balance.

The following information has been taken from the financial statements at the year end:

	£
Revenue for the year	357,700
Purchases for the year	258,775
Trade receivables	34,300
Trade payables	27,650

REQUIRED

(a) (i) Calculate the trade receivable days. State the formula used.

Formula

....

....

Calculation

....

....

(ii) Calculate the trade payable days. State the formula used.

Formula

....

....

Calculation

....

....

(b)   Evaluate the liquidity position of Friel Ltd as shown by the trade receivable and trade
        payable days. The industry average ratios are: trade receivables = 37 days; trade
        payables = 33 days.

....

....

....

....

....

....

....

....

....

....

....

....

....

....

....

....

....

....

....

....

....

....

CHAPTER 19: BUDGETS AND BUDGETARY CONTROL

1. Ela runs a catering company. She would like to buy some new kitchen equipment in April at a cost of £3,000. However, she is not sure whether she will have enough cash available. She provides the following budgeted information.

	March	April
	£	£
Sales	6,200	5,800
Purchases of supplies	3,200	2,800
Operating expenses	1,550	1,360

    Additional information

    (1) Sales are made on the basis of 20% cash and 80% credit. Credit customers will pay one month after the sale.

    (2) All purchases of supplies are on credit. Ela pays her suppliers one month after the purchase of supplies.

    (3) Operating expenses are paid in the month in which they are incurred.

    (4) Ela depreciates all kitchen equipment at 20% per annum on cost. She depreciates her existing equipment by £250 per month.

    (5) Ela calculates that the bank balance at 31 March will be £1,855.

REQUIRED

Prepare a cash budget for April **only** and state if Ela can afford the kitchen equipment.

Cash budget for April

£

....

....

....

....

....

....

....

....

....

....

....

....

....

Can Ela afford the kitchen equipment?

....

....

2. Wyvern Office Ltd is a supplier of stationery and office products to business and personal customers. The managing director wishes to purchase a new computer system to handle all aspects of the company's operations.

The estimated costs of the new computer system are:

Details	£	Terms
Computer hardware	15,000	A deposit of 30% payable in August, the remainder payable in October
Computer software	2,500	Payable in September
Staff training costs	2,000	Payable in September
Annual maintenance contract	1,800	The contract is to be paid in equal monthly instalments starting in September

Additional information

(1)

Forecasts for:	July £	August £	September £	October £
Sales	35,000	33,000	38,000	42,000
Purchases of supplies	19,000	18,000	21,000	27,000
Operating expenses	4,500	5,000	6,000	7,000

(2) Sales are made on the basis of 30% cash and 70% credit. Credit customers are expected to pay one month after the sale.

(3) Purchases are paid one month after purchase.

(4) Operating expenses are paid in the month they are incurred.

(5) Depreciation of non-current assets is estimated to be £1,000 per month.

(6) The company intends to pay an interim dividend of £20,500 in September.

(7) The managing director has negotiated an overdraft facility of £10,000.

(8) The bank balance at 31 July is calculated to be £1,200.

REQUIRED

(a)   Prepare a cash budget for **each** of the three months, August, September and October, assuming the company purchases the computer system.

....

....

....

....

....

....

....

....

....

....

....

....

....

....

....

....

....

....

....

....

(b)   Advise the managing director whether or not the company needs to arrange additional finance to purchase the computer system. Justify your advice.

....

....

....

....

....

....

....

....

....

....

3.

> The directors of Layton Ltd have to repay a loan cf £300,000 in August 20X2. They propose to make a rights issue on 1 July 20X2 on the basis of 1 new share for every 4 shares in issue at a premium of 20p per share.
>
> The share capital of Layton Ltd at 30 June 20X2 was:
>
> | | £ |
> |---|---|
> | Ordinary shares of 50p each, fully paid | 750,000 |

REQUIRED

(a) Calculate the cash to be received from the rights issue assuming that it is fully subscribed.

....

....

....

....

> The directors of Layton Ltd propose to pay a dividend in September 20X2 of 4p per share based on the shares in issue in September 20X2.

REQUIRED

(b) Calculate the amount of the dividend to be paid.

....

....

....

....

The directors of Layton Ltd are concerned about the liquidity of the business. They provide the following forecast information for each of the 6 months ending 30 September 20X2.

Forecasts for:	April	May	June	July	August	September
	£	£	£	£	£	£
Sales	60,000	80,000	90,000	100,000	95,000	85,000
Purchases of inventory	35,000	45,000	50,000	55,000	52,500	50,000
Operating expenses (excluding depreciation)	15,000	17,500	20,000	22,500	22,500	21,000
Depreciation	1,750	1,750	1,750	1,750	1,750	1,750

(1) Sales are made on the basis of 20% cash and the remainder on credit. Of the credit customers, 75% pay one month after the sale and the remainder two months after the sale.

(2) Purchases of inventory are paid one month after the purchase.

(3) Operating expenses are paid in the month they are incurred.

(4) The bank balance at 1 July 20X2 is expected to be £23,500.

REQUIRED

(c) Prepare a cash budget for each of the three months ending 30 September 20X2.

Assume that the rights issue is fully subscribed and that the proposed dividend is paid.

Cash budget for Layton Ltd for the three months ending 30 September 20X2

	July £	August £	September £

(d)   Assess the liquidity position of Layton Ltd as shown by the cash budget.

....

....

....

....

....

....

....

....

....

....

....

....

....

....

....

4. Rachel Malik has prepared a cash budget for her business for the next six months.

The following is an extract for each month.

	January £	February £	March £	April £	May £	June £
Opening bank balance	1,220	1,670	740	(1,680)	(3,410)	(2,580)
Net cash flow	450	(930)	(2,420)	(1,730)	830	950
Closing bank balance	1,670	740	(1,680)	(3,410)	(2,580)	(1,630)

REQUIRED

Evaluate **two** reasons why Rachel Malik has prepared this cash budget.

....

....

....

....

....

....

....

....

....

....

....

....

....

CHAPTER 20: THE IMPACT OF COMPUTER TECHNOLOGY IN ACCOUNTING

1. Progress Limited is planning to introduce an integrated computer accounting system. The Operations Director has been told about all the advantages by the software company but is anxious to know about about the possible disadvantages. You are to state **two** possible disadvantages of this proposal and explain how they could cause problems within the company.

disadvantage 1...

....

....

....

....

....

....

....

....

disadvantage 2...

....

....

....

....

....

....

....

....

2.   Describe and explain **two** situations where a computerised inventory control system may not have recorded changes in the inventory levels of a business.

situation 1...

....

....

....

....

....

....

....

....

....

situation 2...

....

....

....

....

....

....

....

....

....

Answers

Unit 1 answers

CHAPTERS 1-6: DOUBLE-ENTRY PROCEDURES; BUSINESS DOCUMENTS

1. **(a)** Two from:

    - To quantify items such as sales and expenses showing what transactions have happened in the past

    - To record amounts due from trade receivables and due to trade payables and to take appropriate action

    - To help reduce the risk of fraud by keeping detailed records which are maintained by several different individuals

    - To enable the production of financial statements – income statement and balance sheet

    - To enable the production of forecasts for the future – forecast, or budgeted accounts – based on information from previous years

    - To monitor performance by comparing actual outcomes with forecast outcomes, and to take appropriate action

    - To provide information to the owner of the business and other stakeholders

    (b) Three from:

    - bank: to ensure that borrowings are likely to be repaid

    - suppliers: to check the likelihood of receiving payment

    - customers: to check that the business can supply them with orders made

    - employees: to ensure that they will be paid their wages

    - trade unions: to ensure that employees are being offered the right terms and conditions

    - tax authorities: to ensure that tax due by the business on profits and for Value Added Tax has been paid

    - local community: to ensure that jobs are provided in the area

    - competitors: to compare the profitability of the business with their own

    - investors: to assess the return on their investment and the safety of their investment

    - potential investors: to assess the suitability of investing in the business

2.   **(a)**

Transaction	Source document
Alcaria sold goods to Sam Brass for £275	Sales invoice
Sam Brass returned goods valued at £84 to Alcaria	Sales credit note
Sam Brass sent a cheque, after deducting a cash discount of £18, to Alcaria to clear the balance owing at 1 May	Bank paying-in slip counterfoil

(b)

Dr   **Sam Brass**   **Cr**

Date	Details	£	Date	Details	£
1 May	Balance b/d	745	16 May	Sales returns	84
7 May	Sales	275	24 May	Discount allowed	18
			24 May	Bank	727
			31 May	Balance c/d	191
		1,020			1,020
1 Jun	Balance b/d	191			

3. **(a)**

Item	Source document	Account to be debited	Account to be credited
1	Cheque counterfoil	Wages	Cash book/Bank
2	Purchases credit note	Trade payable/ Purchases ledger control account*	Purchases returns

* see chapter 11

(b)

Dr   Fashion Frocks   Cr

Date	Details	£	Date	Details	£
12 June	Bank	1,205	1 June	Balance b/d	1,275
12 June	Discount received	70	8 June	Purchases	950
18 June	Purchases returns	150	23 June	Purchases	650
30 June	Balance c/d	1,450			
		2,875			2,875
			1 July	Balance b/d	1,450

4.   **(a)**

Transaction	Source document
Shoes from a manufacturer purchased on credit	Purchases invoice
Michel returned shoes to a manufacturer which had previously been purchased on credit	Purchases credit note
Cash and cheques deposited by Michel into the business bank account	Bank paying-in slip counterfoil
Michel paid a supplier by cheque	Cheque counterfoil
Michel sold 50 pairs of trainers to a sports centre. Payment will be made next month	Sales invoice

(b)

Transaction	Account to be debited	Account to be credited
A new shop till purchased from AJ Supplies on credit for £1,000	Shop equipment/fittings	AJ Supplies - trade payable
£5,000 paid into the business bank account from Michel's savings	Bank	Capital
Paid £1,200 to Shoe Traders, a supplier, in settlement of the account balance	Shoe Traders - trade payable	Bank
Paid shop rent of £750 by cheque	Rent	Bank

5. • A business will extract a trial balance on a regular basis to check the arithmetic accuracy of the book-keeping

• However, a trial balance does not prove the complete accuracy of the accounting records – there are six types of errors that are not shown by the trial balance:

1. Error of omission – a business transaction completely omitted from the accounting records

2. Reversal of entries – debit and credit entries have been made in the accounts but on the wrong side of the two accounts concerned

3. Mispost/error of commission – a transaction is entered to the wrong person's account

4. Error of principle – a transaction is entered in the wrong type of account

5. Error of original entry (or transcription) the amount of a transaction is entered incorrectly in both accounts

6. Compensating error – two errors cancel each other out

• A trial balance is also used as the starting point in the production of the financial statements of a business – income statement and balance sheet

6.   (a)

Dr								Bank Account						Cr
Date **20X7**	**Details**	**Discount** **£**	**Bank** **£**	**Date** **20X7**	**Details**	**Discount** **£**	**Bank** **£**
26 Apr	Balance b/d		246	27 Apr	J Khan		332
27 Apr	A Monro		116	30 Apr	Raven Ltd	16	746
28 Apr	A Syed	10	425				
30 Apr	Balance c/d		291				
		10	1,078			16	1,078
				1 May	Balance b/d		291

Dr			Discount Allowed			Cr
Date **20X7**	**Details**	**£**	**Date** **20X7**	**Details**	**£**
30 Apr	Bank	10			

Dr			Discount Received			Cr
Date **20X7**	**Details**	**£**	**Date** **20X7**	**Details**	**£**
			30 Apr	Bank	16

(b)

Dr			A Monro			Cr
Date **20X7**	**Details**	**£**	**Date** **20X7**	**Details**	**£**
6 Apr	Sales	316	27 Apr	Bank	116
			30 Apr	Balance c/d	200
		316			316
1 May	Balance b/d	200			

Dr   **A Syed**   **Cr**

Date 20X7	Details	£	Date 20X7	Details	£
8 Apr	Sales	435	28 Apr	Bank	425
			28 Apr	Discount allowed	10
		435			435

Dr   **J Khan**   **Cr**

Date 20X7	Details	£	Date 20X7	Details	£
27 Apr	Bank	332	1 Apr	Balance b/d	332
30 Apr	Balance c/d	454	11 Apr	Purchases	454
		786			786
			1 May	Balance b/d	454

Dr   **Raven Ltd**   **Cr**

Date 20X7	Details	£	Date 20X7	Details	£
30 Apr	Bank	746	13 Apr	Purchases	762
30 Apr	Discount received	16			
		762			762

CHAPTER 7: THE MAIN CASH BOOK

1. (i)   Direct debit

Payments made by the bank from the account of their customer. It is the payee, or beneficiary, who originates the payment on the written instructions of the customer. Direct debits can be for fixed or variable amounts, and the payment dates can alter.

(ii)   Standing order

Regular payments – eg monthly, weekly – made by the bank from the account of their customer. Payments are for fixed amounts, on the written instructions of the bank's customer.

2.

Cash Book

Dr						Cr				
Date 20X7	Details	Discount £	Cash £	Bank £		Date 20X7	Details	Discount £	Cash £	Bank £
3 Aug	Balance b/d		286			3 Aug	Balance b/d			3,472
4 Aug	Sales		334			3 Aug	Rent			760
5 Aug	Cash	C		500		5 Aug	Bank	C	500	
5 Aug	Murphy Ltd	15		1,475		8 Aug	Rates			223
10 Aug	Bank	C	400			8 Aug	JJ Supplies	10		490
10 Aug	Balance c/d			3,370		10 Aug	Cash	C		400
						10 Aug	Wages		480	
						10 Aug	Balance c/d		40	
		15	1,020	5,345				10	1,020	5,345
11 Aug	Balance b/d		40			11 Aug	Balance b/d			3,370

3.   (a) and (b)

Dr	**Emma Maxwell Cash Book**				Cr						
Date 20X3	Details	Discount £	Cash £	Bank £	Date 20X3	Details		Discount £	Cash £	Bank £
1 Mar	Balance b/d		200		1 Mar	Balance b/d				1,898
6 Mar	Court Ltd			1,236	2 Mar	Lindum Supplies		6		254
13 Mar	H Sweeney	BACS	10		896	11 Mar	Rent				550
14 Mar	Sales		639		27 Mar	Wages			155	
28 Mar	Sales		786		20 Mar	Wyvern Council	SO			195
24 Mar	Mills & Co Ltd	BACS		477	21 Mar	Bank interest				45
31 Mar	Cash	C		1,270	31 Mar	Bank	C		1,270	
					31 Mar	Balances c/d			200	937
		10	1,625	3,879				6	1,625	3,879
1 Apr	Balances b/d		200	937						

(c)

Dr	**Discount Allowed Account**		Cr		
Date 20X3	Details	£	Date 20X3	Details	£
31 Mar	Cash book	10			

Dr	**Discount Received Account**		Cr		
Date 20X3	Details	£	Date 20X3	Details	£
			31 Mar	Cash book	6

CHAPTER 8: BANK RECONCILIATION STATEMENTS

1. (a)

Dr		Cash book (bank columns)		Cr
Details	**£**	**Details**		**£**
Balance b/d	743	Bank charges		25
Alportal Ltd BACS	455	Wyvern Council	DD	220
A Alta adjustment	9	L Johnson		105
		Balance c/d		857
	1,207			1,207
Balance b/d	857			

(b)   **Bank reconciliation statement at 27 April 20X1**

	£
Balance at bank as per cash book	857
Add: unpresented cheque	
S Brass	126
	983
Less: outstanding lodgement	
takings	275
Balance at bank as per bank statement	708

(c)   Three from:

- By comparing the transactions in the cash book and bank statement, any errors will be found and can be corrected (or advised to the bank, if the bank statement is wrong).

- The bank statement is an independent accounting record, therefore it will assist in deterring fraud by providing a means of verifying the cash book balance.

- By writing the cash book up-to-date, Jayne Carter's business has an amended figure for the bank balance to be shown in the trial balance.

- Unpresented cheques over six months old – out-of-date cheques – can be identified and written back in the cash book (any cheque dated more than six months ago will not be paid by the bank).

- It is good practice to prepare a bank reconciliation statement each time a bank statement is received so that any queries can be resolved.

2. (a)

Dr	Cash book (bank columns)			Cr
Details	**£**	**Details**		**£**
Adjustment	645	Balance b/d		2,408
Balance c/d	2,837	A-Z Finance Ltd	DD	485
		Bank interest and charges		124
		Adjustment		465
	3,482			3,482
		Balance b/d		2,837

(b)

Susana Villona

Bank reconciliation statement at 30 September 20X4

	£
Balance at bank as per cash book	(2,837)
Add: unpresented cheque	
rent paid	750
	(2,087)
Less: outstanding lodgement	
customer's cheque	368
Balance at bank as per bank statement	(2,455)

(c)
- Her bank account is overdrawn and so the bank is a stakeholder in her business.
- The bank will wish to consider the profitability and liquidity of her business to ensure that the lending is safe.
- The bank will consider whether her business has the ability to meet the interest charged and to make repayment of the overdraft.
- The financial statements can assist the bank in deciding whether to allow the continuance of the overdraft facility.
- The bank may be able to give advice on the future financial management of her business.

CHAPTER 9: INTRODUCTION TO FINANCIAL STATEMENTS

1.

Samantha Giardino
Income Statement
for the year ended 31 December 20X7

	£	£
Revenue		188,622
Opening inventories	21,945	
Purchases	110,233	
	132,178	
Less Closing inventories	18,762	
Cost of sales		113,416
Gross Profit		75,206
Less expenses:		
Salaries	37,390	
Heating and lighting	4,276	
Rent and rates	6,849	
Sundry expenses	1,283	
Vehicle expenses	3,562	
		53,360
Profit for the year		21,846

Balance Sheet as at 31 December 20X7

	£	£	£
Non-current Assets			
Vehicles			20,450
Office equipment			10,960
			31,410
Current Assets			
Inventories		18,762	
Trade receivables		24,365	
		43,127	
Less Current Liabilities			
Trade payables	19,871		
Bank overdraft	2,454		
		22,325	
Net Current Assets			20,802
Net Assets			52,212
Financed by			
Capital			
Opening capital			51,283
Add Profit for the year			21,846
			73,129
Less Drawings			20,917
			52,212

2.   (a)

Alan Castle
Income Statement
for the year ended 30 June 20X3

	£	£
Gross Profit		55,430
Add discount received		210
		55,640
Less expenses:		
Salaries and wages	47,390	
Office expenses	2,750	
Vehicle expenses	6,840	
Bank charges	570	
		57,550
Loss for the year		1,910

(b)

Dr			**Capital Account**			Cr
20X3	Details	£	20X3	Details	£	
30 Jun	Loss	1,910	30 Jun	Balance b/d	42,170	
30 Jun	Drawings	8,460				
30 Jun	Balance c/d	31,800				
		42,170			42,170	
			1 Jul	Balance b/d	31,800	

3.

PQ Trading
Balance Sheet as at 30 September 20X2

	£	£	£
Non-current Assets			
Property			175,000
Office equipment			16,450
			191,450
Current Assets			
Inventories		16,345	
Trade receivables		24,540	
Cash		496	
		41,381	
Less Current Liabilities			
Trade payables	21,364		
Bank overdraft	5,145	26,509	14,872
Net Current Assets			206,322
Less Non-current Liabilities			
Mortgage on business premises			100,000
Net Assets			106,322
Financed by			
Capital		W1	102,772
Add Profit for the year			24,550
Less Drawings			21,000
			106,322

W1 Capital   106,322 + 21,000 − 24,550 = 102,772

CHAPTER 10: THE GENERAL JOURNAL AND CORRECTION OF ERRORS

1.

Dr   **Suspense account**   **Cr**

Details	£	Details	£
Purchases returns	9	Purchases	100
Discount received	70		
Balance (difference)	21		
	100		100

2. (a)

Dr   **Suspense account**   **Cr**

Details	£	Details		£
Discount allowed	100	Balance b/d	W1	458
Vehicle expenses	86	Vehicle expenses		68
Discount received	40	Wages		350
Rent paid	500	Drawings		350
Rent received	500			
	1,226			1,226

W1 Balance b/d (trial balance difference) 364,859 − 364,401 = 458

(b)

Error	Increase profit £	Reduce profit £	No effect on profit (✓)
(1)	100		
(2)	18		
(3)	40		
(4)		175	
(5)	1,000		
(6)		700	

CHAPTER 11: CONTROL ACCOUNTS

1. (a)

Dr					
				Purchases Ledger Control Account	Cr
Date	**Details**	**£**	**Date**	**Details**	**£**
30 April	Cash book	37,396	1 April	Balance b/d	33,154
30 April	Returns outwards	1,532	30 April	Purchases day book	42,805
30 April	Discounts received	741	30 April	Cash book	842
30 April	Contra: sales ledger	585			
30 April	Balance c/d	36,547			
		76,801			76,801
			1 May	Balance b/d	36,547

(b) • The balance of purchases ledger control account should agree with the total of the individual account balances in purchases ledger.

• If these do not agree there will be errors in the purchases ledger, in the purchases ledger control account, or in both.

(c) One from:

• Some types of errors (mispost/error of commission, compensating error, error of omission, error of original entry) will not be revealed by purchases ledger control account; thus the ledger accounts will be thought to be correct when they are not.

• Purchases ledger control account may indicate that there is an error within the ledger section, but will not pinpoint where the error has occurred.

2. (a)

Dr					Sales Ledger Control Account		Cr
Date	**Details**		**£**	**Date**	**Details**		**£**
1 June	Balance b/d		45,027	30 June	Sales returns day book		1,475
30 June	Sales day book		61,322	30 June	Bank		55,396
30 June	Bank		345	30 June	Discounts allowed		1,027
				30 June	Contra: purchases ledger		824
				30 June	Balance c/d		47,972
			106,694				106,694
1 July	Balance b/d		47,972				

(b) • The balance of her sales ledger control account should agree with the total of the individual account balances in sales ledger.

 • If these do not agree there will be errors in the sales ledger, in the sales ledger control account, or in both.

(c) Two from:

 • Mispost/error of commission – where a transaction is entered in the wrong person's account (eg J Smith instead of J Smithson).

 • Compensating error – where two errors cancel each other out (eg an overcast of £100 on one sales ledger account is cancelled out by an undercast on another sales ledger account).

 • Error of omission – where a business transaction has been completely omitted from the accounting records.

 • Error of original entry (or transcription) – the amount of a transaction is entered incorrectly in both accounts (eg an amount for £54 is entered as £45).

3. (a)

Dr				Sales Ledger Control Account		Cr
Date 20X2	Details	£	Date 20X2	Details		£
31 Aug	Balance b/d	18,870	31 Aug	Balance adjustment	W1	90
31 Aug	Sales day book	1,000	31 Aug	Discount allowed		125
31 Aug	Bank (returned cheque)	395	31 Aug	Bad debt		220
			31 Aug	Purchases ledger (contra)		175
			31 Aug	Balance c/d		19,655
		20,265				20,265
1 Sep	Balance b/d	19,655				

W1 Balance adjustment   18,870 − 18,780 = 90

(b)   Three from:

- Verifies the arithmetical accuracy of the total at the sales ledger account.
- Provides managers with a total figure for trade receivables.
- Provides a figure for trade receivables for the trial balance and balance sheet.
- Helps in the prevention of fraud.
- Helps in the location of errors within individual sales ledger accounts.

CHAPTER 12: ADJUSTMENTS TO FINANCIAL STATEMENTS

1.   (a)   Accrued expenses

Accrued expenses are amounts due in an accounting period which are unpaid at the end of that period.

In financial statements accrued expenses are:

- added to the expense in the trial balance before listing it in the income statement – in this way, profit for the year will be reduced

- shown as a current liability in the year end balance sheet (where they may be included in a section for 'other payables').

(b)   Prepaid expenses

Prepaid expenses are payments made in advance of the accounting period to which they relate.

In financial statements prepaid expenses are:

- deducted from the expenses in the trial balance before listing it in the income statement – in this way, profit for the year will be increased

- shown as a current asset in the year end balance sheet (where they may be included in a section for 'other receivables').

2.

Shelley Smith
Income Statement for the year ended 31 December 20X3

	£	£
Revenue		124,380
Returns inwards		(490)
Net Revenue		123,890
Opening inventories	27,170	
Purchases	85,210	
Carriage inwards	1,340	
Returns outwards	(1,520)	
	112,200	
Closing inventories	(29,210)	
Cost of sales		82,990
Gross profit		40,900
Add: Discounts received		970
		41,870
Less Expenses:		
Discounts allowed	460	
General expenses	16,450	
Depreciation of shop fittings W1	1,500	
Rent and rates W2	10,080	
Telephone expenses	1,260	
		29,750
Profit for the year		12,120

W1	Depreciation of shop fittings	$8,300 - 800 = 7,500 \div 5 = 1,500$
W2	Rent and rates	$10,160 + 250 - 330 \ (1,320 \div 3 \text{ months}) = 10,080$

3. (a)

Richard Farley:
Income Statement for the year ended 31 March 20X3

		£	£
Revenue			154,360
Returns inwards			(430)
Net revenue			153,930
Opening inventories		24,830	
Purchases		76,250	
Carriage inwards		850	
		101,930	
Closing inventories		(26,450)	
Cost of sales			75,480
Gross profit			78,450
Add: Discounts received			790
			79,240
Less Expenses:			
Discounts allowed		180	
General expenses		11,470	
Heating and lighting		2,720	
Rent and rates	W1	13,210	
Wages and salaries	W2	38,090	
Depreciation of shop fittings	W3	2,680	
Bad debt written off		240	
			68,590
Profit for the year			10,650

W1	Rent and rates	18,390 − 5,180 = 13,210
W2	Wages and salaries	37,260 + 830 = 38,090
W3	Depreciation of shop fittings	(15,200 − 1,800) ÷ 5 = 2,680

(b)

Richard Farley: Balance Sheet as at 31 March 20X3

		£	£
Non-current Assets			
Shop fittings at cost		15,200	
Shop fittings provision for depreciation	W1	8,040	
			7,160
Current Assets			
Inventories		26,450	
Trade receivables	W2	3,300	
Prepaid expense (Other receivables)	W3	5,180	
		34,930	
Current Liabilities			
Bank overdraft	W4	80	
Trade payables		6,220	
Accrued expense (Other payables)		830	
		7,130	
Net Current Assets			27,800
			34,960
Non-current Liabilities			
Bank loan (repayable September 20X8)			(7,600)
Net Assets			27,360
Financed by			
Capital at 1 April 20X2			29,250
Increase in capital			2,500
Add Profit for the year			10,650
			42,400
Less Drawings			15,040
			27,360

W1	Depreciation of shop fittings	$5,360 + 2,680 = 8,040$
W2	Trade receivables	$3,540 - 240 = 3,300$
W3	Prepaid expense	$10,360 \div 2 = 5,180$
W4	Bank overdraft	$2,580 - 2,500 = 80$

4.

Susie Leah: Balance Sheet as at 31 December 20X6

		£000	£000
Non-current Assets			
Property at cost			220
Office equipment at cost		60	
Office equipment provision for depreciation		(35)	
			25
			245
Current Assets			
Inventories		18	
Trade receivables	W1	12	
Prepaid expenses (Other receivables)		3	
		33	
Current Liabilities			
Trade payables		18	
Accrued expenses (Other payables)	W2	5	
Bank overdraft	W3	4	
		27	
Net Current Assets			6
			251
Non-current Liabilities			
Mortgage on premises (repayable 20X9)			(150)
Net Assets			101
Financed by			
Capital at 1 January 20X5			103
Add Profit for the year	W4		18
			121
Less Drawings			20
			101

W1	Trade receivables	$15 - 2 - 1 = 12$
W2	Accrued expenses	$2 + 3 = 5$
W3	Bank overdraft	$6 - 2 = 4$
W4	Profit for the year	$22 - 3 - 1 = 18$

5. (a)

	Effect on profit	
	£	£
Profit for the year		**25,000**
1. Wages owing	(1,480)	
2. Rent paid in advance	1,100	
3. Motor vehicle depreciation	(7,700)	
4. Inventories understated	2,000	
5. Loan repayment	no effect	
6. Cheque received from trade receivable	no effect	
7. Bad debt written off	(250)	
Adjusted profit for the year		18,670

(b)

Lydia Duarte: Balance Sheet as at 30 September 20X5

		£	£
Non-current Assets			
Vehicles at cost		38,500	
Vehicles provision for depreciation	W1	23,100	
			15,400
Current Assets			
Inventories	W2	38,430	
Trade receivables	W3	23,260	
Prepaid expenses (Other receivables)	W4	1,830	
		63,520	
Current Liabilities			
Bank overdraft	W5	2,350	
Loan	W6	11,000	
Trade payables		16,150	
Accrued expenses (Other payables)	W7	2,070	
		31,570	
Net Current Assets			31,950
Net Assets			47,350

Financed by

Capital at 1 October 20X4	42,440
Add Profit for the year	18,670
	61,110
Less Drawings	13,760
	47,350

W1	Depreciation of vehicles	15,400 + 7,700 = 23,100
W2	Inventories	36,430 + 2,000 = 38,430
W3	Trade receivables	24,310 − 800 − 250 = 23,260
W4	Prepaid expenses	730 + 1,100 = 1,830
W5	Bank overdraft	2,150 + 1,000 − 800 = 2,350
W6	Loan	12,000 − 1,000 = 11,000
W7	Accrued expenses	590 + 1,480 = 2,070

6. (a)   **private expenses**

Private expenses are where the owner uses business facilities for private purposes – eg telephone or car. The owner will agree the amount that is to be charged to him/her as drawings, while the other part represents a business expense.

In the double-entry accounts, the expense account is credited and the owner's drawings amount is debited with the private amount. The remaining balance of the expense account is then charged to the income statement, after adjustment for any accruals or prepayments. The balance of drawings account is shown on the balance sheet as a deduction from capital and, in the double-entry accounts, is debited to the owner's capital account.

(b)   **goods for owner's use**

When the owner of a business takes some of the goods in which the business trades for his/her own use, the amount is:

– debited to the owner's drawings account

– credited to purchases account

The reason for crediting purchases account is to reduce the amount of purchases and record only those purchases used in the business, which are then matched with the sales derived from them.

Unit 2 answers

CHAPTER 13: BUSINESS ORGANISATIONS

1. *Advantages*

    Two from:

    - Limited liability – if the business fails then Erica will lose only the amount of her investment in the company and, unlike a sole trader or a partnership, her personal assets cannot be taken to pay the debts of the company.

    - Separate legal entity – anyone taking legal action proceeds against the company and not the individual shareholder(s); also, a limited company does not finish when the owner retires or dies – it can be sold on to others.

    - Decision-making – as Erica will be the only shareholder she can continue to take all the decisions; in larger companies this will not be the case.

    - Raising finance – Erica may be able to raise finance more easily from relatives and friends, and from venture capital companies; raising bank loans is usually easier for a company than for a sole trader or partnership.

    - Other factors – a limited company often has a higher status and standing in the business community, and this may allow for expansion in the future.

    Disadvantages

    Two from:

    - Legal and accountancy costs – setting up a private limited company has start-up costs and annual costs will be higher than for a sole trader or partnership.

    - Legal requirements – the administration of a company is greater than for a sole trader/partnership as the company must be registered at Companies House, formal annual financial statements must be produced and filed at Companies House, and the annual financial statements may need to be audited (depending on the size of the business).

    - Published financial statements – Erica must ensure that her accounting records are of a sufficient standard to enable annual financial statements to be completed (her accountant will charge more for preparing the financial statements of a limited company than for a sole trader or partnership), and her annual financial statements will be available through Companies House for anyone to see.

2. Two from:

- **Legal requirements**

  Setting up a private limited company is more complex and start-up costs will be higher than for a sole trader or partnership:

  - the company must be registered at Companies House

  - formal annual financial statements must be prepared and filed at Companies House

  - the annual financial statements may have to be audited, depending on the size of the business

- **Control of the company**

  Jane and Scott's business requires capital of £70,000 but their contribution will be £15,000 each. This means that £40,000 will have to be raised from selling shares or from other forms of finance. If a shareholder buys more than half of all shares in issue, then Jane and Scott will lose control of their business and will not be able to run it as they wish.

- **Dividend payments**

  Outside shareholders will be looking to invest in Jane and Scott's company with a view to receiving income in the form of dividends. This means that Jane and Scott must share the profits with others instead of between themselves.

- **Conclusion**

  Whilst it is far simpler for Jane and Scott to form a partnership, they must weigh up whether or not the disadvantages of forming a company are outweighed by the benefits of limited liability which a company will give.

CHAPTER 14: ACCOUNTING CONCEPTS AND INVENTORY VALUATION

1. (a) (i) **Prudence**

This concept – also known as conservatism in accounting – requires that financial statements should always, where there is any doubt, report a conservative (lower) figure for profit and the valuation of assets. To this end, profits are not to be anticipated and should only be recognised when it is reasonably certain that they will be actually made; at the same time, all known liabilities should be provided for. 'Anticipate no profit, but anticipate all losses' is a summary of the prudence concept.

(ii) **Consistency**

This concept requires that, when a business adopts particular accounting policies, it should continue to use such policies consistently. For example, a business that decides to make a provision for depreciation at ten per cent per year, using the straight-line method, should continue to use that method for future financial statements for this asset. However, having chosen a particular policy, a business is entitled to make changes provided there are good reasons for so doing, and a note to the financial statements would explain what has happened.

(b)   The application of the prudence concept to the preparation of the financial statements of a business prevents an over-optimistic presentation of the assets, liabilities and profit.

Examples of the use of the prudence concept include:

- accrual of expenses and income, where an estimate is made of the amount
- prepayment of expenses and income, where an estimate is made of the amount
- inventory valuation – at the lower of cost and net realisable value
- depreciation of non-current assets
- bad debts written off
- provision for doubtful debts

The application of the consistency concept ensures that a direct comparison between the financial statements of different years can be made. The use of ratio analysis to interpret the financial statements of a business over two or more years is meaningful where the consistency concept has been applied.

Examples of the use of the consistency concept include:

- inventory valuation
- depreciation of non-current assets
- provision for doubtful debts
- the application of the materiality concept (which establishes which items are of sufficient value to be recorded separately in the financial statements)

2.   (a)

Cost 100 x £15	=		£1,500
Net realisable value	100 x £17.50 =		£1,750
Less advertising costs			£300
			£1,450

Applying the rule of 'lower of cost and net realisable value', the inventory should be valued at £1,450 for the financial statements for the year ended 31 December 20X4.

(b)   One from:

- prudence
- consistency
- cost
- materiality

3.

Item	Effect on profit	Concept
(1) Fee for audit and tax advice	(7,500)	Accruals
(2) Rent	1,500	Accruals
(3) Depreciation	(7,000)	Consistency/Prudence
(4) Inventories	(200)	Consistency/Prudence
(5) Bad debt	(2,000)	Prudence/Realisation

Tutorial note: the assumption is that the business is a going concern and that all amounts are considered to be material.

CHAPTER 15: FURTHER ASPECTS OF FINANCIAL STATEMENTS

1. (a)   21,040 x 3% = £631.20

(b)

	£
Closing provision	631.20
Opening provision	550.80
Increase in provision	80.40

∴ profit for the year ended 31 October 20X8 will be reduced by £80.40.

(c)

	£
Trade receivables	21,040.00
Less provision for doubtful debts	631.20
Net trade receivables to be shown in the balance sheet	20,408.80

2. (a) (i)

		£
vehicles at cost		74,000
less depreciation to 1 January 20X3		33,500
carrying amount		40,500
depreciation charge for year = 40,500 x 30%		12,150

(ii)

		£
machinery at cost		37,000
depreciation charge for year = 37,000 x 20%		7,400

(b)

KAREN
BALANCE SHEET (EXTRACT) AS AT 31 DECEMBER 20X3

Non-current Assets		£	£
Vehicles at cost		74,000	
Less provision for depreciation	W1	45,650	
Net book value			28,350
Machinery at cost		37,000	
Less provision for depreciation	W2	19,650	
Net book value			17,350
			45,700

W1 Vehicles – provision for depreciation: 33,500 + 12,150 = 45,650

W2 Machinery – provision for depreciation: 12,250 + 7,400 = 19,650

Tutorial note: the provision for depreciation at the start of the year cannot be checked back to the cost price of the non-current assets as it is likely that items of vehicles and machinery will have been purchased at various times.

3.   (a)

			£
	Cost		12,000
Less	Depreciation		5,250
Equals	Net book value		6,750
	Sale proceeds		6,500
Equals	Loss on disposal		250

(b)

	£
Cost: 46,000 – disposals 12,000 + addition 16,250 =	50,250
Depreciation: 22,000 – 5,250 =	16,750
	33,500

Depreciation charge for year = 33,500 x 25% =	8,375

4.

ALEX MUNRO

INCOME STATEMENT FOR THE YEAR ENDED 30 APRIL 20X3

		£	£
Gross profit			86,245
Add income:			
Bad debts recovered			195
Rent received	W1		1,820
Decrease in provision for doubtful debts	W2		150
			88,410
Less expenses:			
Wages		33,470	
Bad debts		255	
Administration expenses		24,075	
Discount allowed		315	
Depreciation of non-current assets	W3	10,000	
Loss on sale of vehicle	W4	750	
			68,865
Profit for the year			19,545

W1   Rent received = 2,360 − 540 paid in advance = 1,820

W2   Provision for doubtful debts = 460 − 310 = 150 reduction in provision

W3   £45,000 provision for depreciation at start of year − £7,500 depreciation on vehicle sold = £37,500, minus £27,500 provision for depreciation at end of year = £10,000 depreciation for year (as shown in income statement)

W4

	£
Net book value (£12,000 − £7,500)	4,500
Sale price	3,750
Loss on sale	750

5.

TAMSIN SMITH

INCOME STATEMENT FOR THE YEAR ENDED 30 JUNE 20X4

		£	£
Gross profit	W1		14,190
Add income:			
Rent received	W2	4,950	
Bad debts recovered		220	
Decrease in provision for doubtful debts	W3	52	
			5,222
			19,412
Less expenses:			
Operating expenses	W4	6,735	
Depreciation: vehicles	W5	4,500	
Depreciation: shop fittings	W6	3,400	
Bad debts		590	
			15,225
Profit for the year			4,187

W1   Gross profit = 14,760 − 570 reduction in closing inventory = 14,190

W2   Rent received = 5,600 − 650 paid in advance = 4,950

W3   Provision for doubtful debts = 8,310 − 590 = 7,720 x 2.5% = 193 − 245 = 52 decrease in provision

W4   Operating expenses = 6,240 + 495 = 6,735

W5   Provision for depreciation: vehicles = 32,000 − 14,000 = 18,000 x 25% = 4,500

W6   Provision for depreciation: shop fittings = 17,000 x 20% = 3,400

CHAPTER 16: PREPARING SOLE TRADER FINANCIAL STATEMENTS

1.

ANTON BUSZCZAK
INCOME STATEMENT FOR THE YEAR ENDED 30 JUNE 20X6

		£	£
Revenue			145,630
Opening inventory		4,525	
Purchases		59,450	
		63,975	
Less Closing inventory		5,385	
Cost of sales			58,590
Gross profit			87,040
Less expenses:			
Vehicle running expenses	W1	3,790	
Rent and rates		12,080	
Office expenses	W2	6,680	
Discounts allowed		580	
Wages and salaries		43,190	
Depreciation: machinery		4,000	
vehicles		8,500	
			78,820
Profit for the year			8,220

BALANCE SHEET AS AT 30 JUNE 20X6

	£	£	£
Non-current Assets	Cost	Prov for dep'n	Net book value
Machinery	25,000	W3 15,000	10,000
Vehicles	33,000	W4 20,700	12,300
	58,000	35,700	22,300
Current Assets			
Inventory		5,385	
Trade receivables		4,155	
Prepaid expenses (Other receivables)		175	
Bank		3,365	
		13,080	
Less Current Liabilities			
Trade payables	10,845		
Accrued expenses (Other payables)	345		
		11,190	
Net Current Assets			1,890
NET ASSETS			24,190
FINANCED BY			
Capital			
Opening capital			28,550
Add Profit for the year			8,220
			36,770
Less Drawings			12,580
			24,190

W1   Vehicle running expenses = 3,965 – 175 = 3,790

W2   Office expenses = 6,335 + 345 = 6,680

W3   Provision for depreciation: machinery = 11,000 + 4,000 = 15,000

W4   Provision for depreciation: vehicles = 12,200 + 8,500 = 20,700

2. (a)
SAMANTHA MARTINEZ
INCOME STATEMENT FOR THE YEAR ENDED 30 SEPTEMBER 20X4

		£	£
Revenue			245,084
Opening inventory		5,893	
Purchases (less £750 goods for own use)		155,277	
		161,170	
Less Closing inventory		7,541	
Cost of sales			153,629
Gross profit			91,455
Add income:			
Bad debts recovered			176
Decrease in provision for doubtful debts	W1		93
			91,724
Less expenses:			
Office salaries	W2	50,643	
Rates and insurance	W3	6,201	
Administration expenses		17,122	
Bad debts		295	
Depreciation: property	W4	4,400	
office equipment	W5	7,125	
			85,786
Profit for the year			5,938

W1 Provision for doubtful debts = 18,400 trade receivables x 3% provision = 552 – 645 = £93 decrease in provision

W2 Office salaries = 50,133 + 510 = 50,643

W3 Rates and insurance = 6,433 – 232 = 6,201

W4 Provision for depreciation: property = 220,000 x 2% = 4,400

W5 Provision for depreciation: office equipment = 45,000 – 16,500 = 28,500 x 25% = 7,125

(b)

Capital	£
Opening capital	160,500
Add Profit for the year	5,938
	166,438
Less Drawings (plus £750 goods for own use)	22,900
	143,538

3.

CHARLOTTE LEE
INCOME STATEMENT FOR THE YEAR ENDED 31 DECEMBER 20X5

		£	£
Gross profit	W1		67,606
Add income:			
Rent received	W2		7,244
Profit on sale of vehicle	W3		270
			75,120
Less expenses:			
Bad debts		245	
Operating expenses	W4	25,354	
Wages	W5	40,687	
Depreciation: vehicle	W6	1,920	
fixtures and fittings	W7	4,960	
Increase in provision for doubtful debts	W8	158	
			73,324
Profit for the year			1,796

W1   Gross profit = 67,386 − 400 inventory reduction + 620 drawings = 67,606

W2   Rent received = 7,864 − 620 paid in advance = 7,244

W3   Profit on sale of vehicle = 15,000 − 5,400 = 9,600 x 20% = 1,920 depreciation for year = 7,680 net book value. 7,950 selling price − 7,680 net book value = 270 profit on sale

W4   Operating expenses = 32,149 − 295 paid in advance − 6,500 purchase of fixtures = 25,354

W5   Wages = 40,231 + 456 owing = 40,687

W6   Provision for depreciation: vehicle = 15,000 − 5,400 = 9,600 x 20% = 1,920

W7   Provision for depreciation: fixtures and fittings = 18,300 + 6,500 = 24,800 x 20% = 4,960

W8   Provision for doubtful debts = 24,200 trade receivables x 4% provision = 968 − 810 = £158 increase in provision

4.

HENRY DUNSTONE
INCOME STATEMENT FOR THE YEAR ENDED 31 MARCH 20X7

		£	£
Revenue			283,135
Less returns			1,068
Net Revenue			282,067
Opening inventory		33,940	
Purchases	W1	134,765	
		168,705	
Less Closing inventory		36,875	
Cost of sales			131,830
Gross profit			150,237
Add income:			
Discounts received			741
			150,978
Less expenses:			
Discounts allowed		862	
Operating expenses		35,336	
Rent and rates	W2	16,072	
Salaries	W3	94,550	
Increase in provision for doubtful debts	W4	386	
Depreciation: fixtures and fittings	W5	4,560	
machinery	W6	7,104	
			158,870
Loss for the year			7,892

BALANCE SHEET AS AT 31 MARCH 20X7

		£	£	£
Non-current Assets		Cost	Prov for dep'n	Net book value
Fixtures and fittings		30,400	13,680	16,720
Machinery		55,500	27,084	28,416
		85,900	40,764	45,136
Current Assets				
Inventory			36,875	
Trade receivables	W7		55,809	
Prepaid expenses (Other receivables)			1,950	
			94,634	
Less Current Liabilities				
Trade payables		49,833		
Accrued expenses (Other payables)		1,465		
Bank overdraft		4,107		
			55,405	
Net Current Assets				39,229
NET ASSETS				84,365
Financed by				
Capital				103,856
Less Loss for the year				7,892
				95,964
Less Drawings	W8			11,599
				84,365

W1   Purchases = 136,240 – 1,475 goods for own use = 134,765

W2   Rent and rates = 18,022 – 1,950 = 16,072

W3   Salaries = 93,085 + 1,465 = 94,550

W4   Provision for doubtful debts = 57,240 x 2.5% = 1,431 – 1,045 = 386 increase in provision

W5   Provision for depreciation: fixtures and fittings = 30,400 x 15% = 4,560

W6   Provision for depreciation: machinery = 55,500 – 19,980 = 35,520 x 20% = 7,104

W7   Trade receivables = 57,240 – 1,431 provision for doubtful debts = 55,809

W8   Drawings = 10,124 + 1,475 goods for own use = 11,599

CHAPTER 17: FINANCIAL STATEMENTS OF LIMITED COMPANIES

1.   (a)   Number of shares currently in issue = £800,000 x 4 = 3,200,000

        Bonus issue = 3,200,000 ÷ 5 = 640,000 x 2 = <u>1,280,000 bonus shares</u>

  (b)

Equity		£ (i)	£ (ii)
Ordinary shares of 25p each fully paid	W1	1,120,000	1,120,000
Share premium		nil	90,000
Revaluation reserve		90,000	nil
Retained earnings		215,000	215,000
		1,425,000	1,425,000

    W1   £800,000 + (1,280,000 shares at 25p each)

    Tutorial note: either answer (i) or (ii) is correct – both share premium and revaluation reserve are capital reserves and can be used for the bonus issue in order to keep retained earnings at their highest level.

2.   (a)   Number of shares currently in issue = £500,000 x 2 = 1,000,000

        Rights issue = 1,000,000 ÷ 4 = 250,000

        Cash to be received = 250,000 x (50p + 20p) = <u>£175,000</u>

  (b)   Number of shares = 1,000,000 + 250,000 = 1,250,000

        Dividend to be paid = 1,250,000 x 6p = <u>£75,000</u>

3.

Axiom plc

Statement of changes in equity for the year ended 30 June 20X5

	Issued Share Capital £	Share Premium £	Retained Earnings £	Total £
At 1 July 20X4	600,000	90,000	330,000	1,020,000
Issue of shares	150,000	90,000		240,000
Profit for the year			365,000	365,000
Equity dividends paid in the year			(220,000)	(220,000)
At 30 June 20X5	750,000	180,000	475,000	1,405,000

4.

Bohan Ltd

Statement of changes in equity for the year ended 31 December 20X2

	Issued Share Capital £	Share Premium £	Retained Earnings £	Total £
At 1 January 20X2	220,000	–	118,000	338,000
Issue of shares	110,000	66,000		176,000
Profit for the year			79,000	79,000
Equity dividends paid in the year			(45,000)	(45,000)
At 31 December 20X2	330,000	66,000	152,000	548,000

5.   (a)   **Equity**   **£**

Ordinary shares of £1 each fully paid   W1   720,000

Share premium   W2   147,000

Retained earnings   128,454

                                                   995,454

W1   600,000 + (rights issue 600,000 ÷ 5) = 720,000 shares of £1 each

W2   120,000 shares x 60p premium = £72,000 + £75,000 existing share premium = £147,000

(b)   **Definition:** Capital reserves are created as a result of a non-trading profit – they cannot be used to fund dividend payments.

Example: Share premium account or revaluation reserve.

(c)   **Definition:** Revenue reserves are profits from trading activities which have been retained in the company to help build the company for the future.

Example: Retained earnings or general reserve.

CHAPTER 18: RATIO ANALYSIS

1.   (a)   *Formula*

$$\frac{\text{Cost of sales}}{\text{Average inventory}}$$

Calculation

Average inventory = (10,350 + 14,150) ÷ 2 = 12,250

Rate of inventory turnover =

$\frac{73,750}{12,250}$ = 6 times per year or 61 days or 2 months

(b)   •   The rate of inventory turnover has fallen from 8 times per year to 6 times per year.

•   This means that inventory is being sold more slowly this year.

•   On the face of it, decreasing inventory turnover indicates a less efficient business as inventory is in the shop for longer before being sold.

2. (a) (i)   *Formula*

Current assets

Current liabilit es

Calculation

$$\frac{105,630 + 162,940}{77,620 + 134,230} = \frac{268,570}{211,850} = 1.27{:}1$$

(ii)   *Formula*

Current assets – inventories

Current liabilities

Calculation

$$\frac{162,940}{77,620 + 134,230} = \frac{162,940}{211,850} = 0.77{:}1$$

(b)   <u>Net current ratio</u>
- Capper Ltd has £1.27 of current assets for each £1 of current liabilities.
- This is lower than the industry average of £1.80 for each £1 of current liabilities.
- Capper Ltd must investigate the make-up of its inventory, trade receivables, and trade payables as a low net current asset ratio could make it difficult for the company to pay its trade payables in the future.

<u>Liquid capital ratio</u>
- Capper Ltd has 77p of liquid assets for each £1 of current liabilities.
- This is lower than the industry average of 90p of liquid assets for each £1 of current liabilities.
- Capper Ltd must investigate the make-up of its inventory and trade payables as a low liquid capital ratio could make it difficult for the company to pay its trade payables in the future.

(c)
- When goods are sold on credit there is a timing difference between making the sale/recording the profit and receiving payment for the sale. This timing difference – based on the accruals concept – has to be financed by the business.
- When goods are bought on credit there is a timing difference between making the purchase and paying for the goods. This timing difference is a benefit to the business but it is usually less than the cost to the business of financing sales.
- Prepaid expenses – based on the accruals concept – increase the profit for the year, but the expense has been paid for from the bank, so reducing the bank balance.
- Capital expenditure on non-current assets reduces the bank balance by a greater amount than the depreciation charge for the asset shown in the income statement.
- Repayment of loans reduces the bank balance but has little effect on profitability (although loan interest paid may be reduced).
- Payment of dividends reduces the bank balance but has no effect on profit for the year.

3. (a) *Formula*

$$\frac{\text{Gross profit}}{\text{Revenue}} \times \frac{100}{1}$$

Calculation

$$\frac{72,000}{240,000} = \frac{100}{1} = 30\%$$

(b) *Formula*

$$\frac{\text{Profit from operations}}{\text{Revenue}} \times \frac{100}{1}$$

alternatively $\quad \dfrac{\text{Profit for the year}}{\text{Revenue}} \times \dfrac{100}{1}$

Calculation

$$\frac{12,000}{240,000} = \frac{100}{1} = 5\%$$

alternatively $\quad \dfrac{9,600}{240,000} = \dfrac{100}{1} = 4\%$

(c) *Formula*

$$\frac{\text{Cost of sales}}{\text{Average inventory}}$$

Calculation

Average inventory = (22,000 + 26,000) ÷ 2 = 24,000

Rate of inventory turnover = $\dfrac{168,000}{24,000}$ = 7 times per year or 52 days or 1.7 months

(d)   <u>Gross profit margin</u>

Possible actions to improve ratio:

–   increase selling prices

–   reduce buying prices

–   a combination of both

Problems:

–   increased selling prices may reduce sales and the profitability of the business

–   reducing buying prices may mean that current suppliers will not continue to supply the product; also the quality of the product may be lowered

<u>Profit in relation to revenue</u>

Possible actions to improve ratio:

–   increase gross profit margin

–   reduce expenses

–   a combination of both

Problems:

–   may be difficult to reduce expenses such as wages

–   reducing expenses may affect sales, eg a cut in advertising

<u>Rate of inventory turnover</u>

Possible actions to improve ratio:

–   reduce inventory levels

–   reduce buying prices

–   a combination of both

Problems:

–   reducing inventory levels could result in items being 'out-of-stock', which will impact on profitability

–   reducing buying prices may mean a lower quality of product, which may impact on sales and profitability

4. (a) (i)   *Formula*

$$\frac{\text{Trade receivables}}{\text{Revenue}} \times 365 \text{ days}$$

Calculation

$$\frac{34,300}{357,700} \times 365 = 35 \text{ days}$$

   (ii)   *Formula*

$$\frac{\text{Trade payables}}{\text{Purchases}} \times 365 \text{ days}$$

Calculation

$$\frac{27,650}{258,775} \times 365 = 39 \text{ days}$$

(b)   <u>Trade receivable days</u>
   - Friel Ltd receives payment from trade receivables in 35 days on average.
   - This is shorter than the industry average of 37 days.
   - In general, the shorter the period the better, and this could indicate that Friel Ltd is more efficient at collecting debts than competitors, or that the company offers shorter terms than others within the industry. Either way, this could mean that Friel Ltd may be losing customers to their competitors.

<u>Trade payable days</u>
   - Friel Ltd pays trade payables in 39 days on average.
   - This is longer than the industry average of 33 days.
   - Whilst longer trade payable days are advantageous to the bank balance, it may mean that Friel is not taking advantage of any cash discounts offered for quick settlement. Also, unless Friel Ltd has negotiated longer credit terms, it may be that suppliers will be reluctant to supply the company until outstanding amounts have been paid – this could be detrimental to Friel's sales and customer service.

<u>Conclusion</u>
As Friel's trade receivable days are shorter than the industry average and trade payable days are longer, there should be no adverse effect on the company's bank balance when compared with their competitors.

CHAPTER 19: BUDGETS AND BUDGETARY CONTROL

1.   **Cash budget for April**

	£
Receipts	
Cash sales 5,800 x 20%	1,160
Credit sales 6,200 x 80%	4,960
	6,120
Payments	
Purchase of supplies	3,200
Operating expenses	1,360
Purchase of kitchen equipment	3,000
	7,560
Net cash flow 6,120 – 7,560	(1,440)
Opening bank balance	1,855
Closing bank balance	415

Ela can afford to buy the new kitchen equipment.

2. (a)

WYVERN OFFICE LTD: CASH BUDGET

		August £	September £	October £
Receipts				
Cash sales	30%	9,900	11,400	12,600
Credit sales	70%	24,500	23,100	26,600
		34,400	34,500	39,200
Payments				
Purchases		19,000	18,000	21,000
Operating expenses		5,000	6,000	7,000
Dividend			20,500	
Computer hardware		4,500		10,500
Computer software			2,500	
Staff training costs			2,000	
Maintenance contract			150	150
		28,500	49,150	38,650
Net cash flow		5,900	(14,650)	550
Opening bank balance		1,200	7,100	(7,550)
Closing bank balance		7,100	(7,550)	(7,000)

(b)
- The managing director does not need to arrange additional finance to purchase the new computer system.
- Provided that the forecasts for the period July to October are accurate the company's bank overdraft should not exceed £7,550, which occurs in August. The overdraft facility of £10,000 should provide a comfortable margin above this maximum overdraft.
- If the company continues to trade profitably after October, the overdraft should decrease month-by-month.

3.   (a)   •   1,500,000 shares at 50p each ÷ 4 = 375,000 shares

•   375,000 new shares at 70p = £262,500

(b)   1,500,000 + 375,000 = 1,875,000 shares x 4p per share = £75,000 dividend

(c)   **Cash budget for Layton Ltd for the three months ending 30 September 20X2**

		July	August	September
		£	£	£
Receipts				
Cash sales		20,000	19,000	17,000
Credit sales - 1 month	W1	54,000	60,000	57,000
Credit sales - 2 months	W2	16,000	18,000	20,000
Rights issue		262,500		
		352,500	97,000	94,000
Payments				
Purchases		50,000	55,000	52,500
Operating expenses		22,500	22,500	21,000
Loan repayment			300,000	
Dividend payment				75,000
		72,500	377,500	148,500
Net cash flow		280,000	(280,500)	(54,500)
Opening bank balance		23,500	303,500	23,000
Closing bank balance		303,500	23,000	(31,500)

W1   July (90,000 x 80%) x 75% = 54,000

August (100,000 x 80%) x 75% = 60,000

September (85,000 x 80%) x 75% = 57,000

W2   July (80,000 x 80%) x 25% = 16,000

August (90,000 x 80%) x 25% = 18,000

September (100,000 x 80%) x 25% = 20,000

(d) • At the end of three months the company has an estimated closing bank overdraft of £31,500.

   • This has been brought about partly because the cash from the rights issue of £262,500 is less than the £300,000 needed to repay the loan.

   • Over the three months the company has gone from a bank balance of £23,500 to an overdraft of £31,500. This is a negative cash flow over the period of £55,000.

   • The three-month period has had three significant cash flows: rights issue, loan repayment, dividend payment. Cash from general trading has produced a positive cash flow over the period: July £17,500, August £19,500, September £20,500.

   • One problem for the company is that 25% of the trade receivables pay two months after sale. By contrast, the company pays all its trade payables in the month after sale. This imbalance means that the company is having to finance the extended credit for 25% of its credit customers.

   • The directors of the company will need to arrange a short-term – probably for six months – overdraft facility to cover the shortfall. Alternatively, they could consider postponing payment of the dividend and/or addressing the two-month credit period allowed to some credit customers.

4.   Two from:

·   **Planning**

By preparing the budget, Rachel will be able to plan for the future and react to changes as they occur. She will need to forecast on a month-by-month basis her receipts from sales and her payments for purchases of supplies and operating expenses, including expenditure for 'one-off' transactions such as the purchase of non-current assets. In Rachel's case, the cash budget shows that she will need to arrange an overdraft facility with the bank for up to £3,500 covering the period March to June and beyond.

·   **Monitoring**

Having prepared the budget, Rachel must compare the actual results. This is so that she can identify variances and take action to modify the operation of the business as time passes, or possibly to change the budget if it becomes unachievable.

·   **Control**

By setting targets for her business, Rachel can use the budget to control her receipts and payments. Where variances occur she can investigate the reason(s) and can take appropriate action.

·   **Decision-making**

By planning ahead through the preparation of her cash budget, Rachel may take decisions about her payments. For example, she may decide to defer some of the payments for March and April in order to reduce her need for an overdraft facility. Alternatively, she may consider seeking other methods of funding – particularly if the expense is for the purchase of non-current assets.

·   **Communication and co-ordination**

In order to prepare the cash budget, Rachel has had to co-ordinate with other budgets, eg sales, purchases, and has had to communicate within the different departments of her business. All departments of the business will have had to contribute towards ensuring that her business achieves its objectives.

CHAPTER 20: THE IMPACT OF COMPUTER TECHNOLOGY IN ACCOUNTING

1. **Two** from the following list, identifying each problem and explaining its possible results:

- **cost**

  There are the capital costs of hardware and software and also the associated revenue costs of training, maintenance and updating.

- **staff opposition**

  Some employees may not like computers and some jobs may be lost as manual processes are automated.

- **vulnerability to system failure**

  If the software crashes or the hardware fails, there will be disruption to the workflow and in a worst case scenario, loss of data which may not have been backed up.

- **errors**

  Although data entry is made simpler with a computer-based system, errors can still occur and go undetected, resulting in a money loss – for example a sales invoice which is understated.

- **security**

  There is always the danger of people hacking into the system from outside, the danger of viruses and the possibility of staff fraud.

- **health and safety**

  The increasing use of computers at work may aggravate the problems of bad backs, eyestrain and muscular complaints such as RSI (Repetitive Strain Injury).

2. **Two** from the following:

- **errors** in inputting data into the computer: eg a wrong amount, wrong account
- **stolen inventory** which would be picked up on a physical count, but not on the computer
- **inventory taken by owner (drawings)** – which would be picked up on a physical count, but not on the computer
- **damaged inventory** – which would be put on one side and identified by a physical count, but not on the computer
- **obsolete inventory** – out-of-date goods which would be put on one side or recycled and identified by a physical count, but not on the computer
- **returned inventory** – returned goods which may have been added to the inventory but not recorded on the computer.